BUILDING DREAMS

CONSULTANTS

Mildred Bailey **Wilma J. Farmer** **George Jurata**
Barbara Burke **Teresa Flores** **Kenneth Smith**
Barbara B. Cramer **Charles Hacker** **Mary Wigner**
P. J. Hutchins

Editorial Director: *Sandra Maccarone*
Senior Editor: *Ronne Kaufman*
Associate Editor: *Eleanor Franklin*
Designed by: *Thomas Vroman Associates, Inc.*
Design Director: *Mary Mars*
Assistant Design Director: *Ruth Riley*
Design Supervisor: *Lillie Caporlingua*
Production Director: *Barbara Arkin*
Production Manager: *Barbara Feuer*

Cover Design: *Thomas Vroman Associates, Inc.* Illustrators: Bill Frake, pp. 14-23; Len Ebert, pp. 25-32; Renee Daily, pp. 34-37; True Kelley, pp. 38-42; N. Jo Smith, pp. 43-48; Jerry Zimmerman, pp. 50-56; Kinuko Craft, pp. 60-70; Allen Eitzen, pp. 72-80; Angela Fernan, pp. 82-85; Joy Friedman, pp. 86-92; Angela Fernan, pp. 94-95; Walter Brooks, pp. 96-104; Melanie Arwin, pp. 106-107; Jan Pyk, pp. 110-118; Nurit Karlin, pp. 120-126; Tien Ho, pp. 128-136; Tom Vroman, pp. 138-139; Ric Del Rossi, pp. 140-143; Lane Yerkes, pp. 144-152; Angela Fernan, pp. 154-155; Yee Lin, pp. 158-168; Angela Fernan, pp. 170-173; Jeffrey Terreson, pp. 174-182; Ethel Gold, pp. 183-191; Melanie Arwin, pp. 192-197; Sal Murdocca, p. 199; Sue Parnell, pp. 200-201; Sue Parnell, pp. 204-212; Reisi Lonette, pp. 214-221; Judy Love, pp. 222-230; True Kelley, pp. 232-233; Freya Tanz, pp. 234-235; Ed Hanke, pp. 236-244; Robbie Stillerman, pp. 250-258; Yee Lin, pp. 260-265; Jeffrey Terreson, pp. 266-267; Ric Del Rossi, pp. 268-271; Allen Davis, pp. 272-280; Angela Fernan, pp. 282-283; Will Harmuth, pp. 284-295.

American Book Company

New York Cincinnati Atlanta Dallas San Francisco

ISBN 0-278-45821-1

5 7 9 11 13 14 12 10 8 6 4

Photo Credits: Mark Godfrey, Magnum, cover and p. 1; Harvey Lloyd, Peter Arnold, pp. 8-9; Bruno Barbey, Magnum, p. 11; Eileen Christelow, Jeroboam, p. 12; Paul Fusco, Magnum, p. 13; Elizabeth Crews, Jeroboam, pp. 58-59; Leo Choplin, Black Star, pp. 108-109; James Karales, Peter Arnold, pp. 156-157; Sid Avery, Shostal, pp. 202-203; Michael Philip Manheim, Photo Researchers, pp. 248-249.

ACKNOWLEDGMENTS

Every reasonable effort has been made to trace the owners of copyright materials in this book, but in some instances this has proven impossible. The publishers will be glad to receive information leading to more complete acknowledgments in subsequent printings of the book, and in the meantime extend their apologies for any omissions.

To American Book Company for "Fire Fighters," adapted from "Hooksies and Smoke Eaters," and "The Necklace," both by Wendy Rydell from *I Earn, Explore, and Excel* from *The Triple "I" Series.* Copyright 1970 by Litton Educational Publishing, Inc. Used and adapted by permission.

To Coward, McCann & Geoghegan, Inc., for "Nate the Great and the Lost List." Adapted by permission of Coward, McCann & Geoghegan, Inc. from *Nate the Great and the Lost List* by Marjorie Weinman Sharmat. Text copyright © 1975 by Marjorie Weinman Sharmat.

To Thomas Y. Crowell Co., Inc., for "How the Sun Came" by Alice Marriott and Carol K. Rachlin. Copyright © 1968 by the authors. From *American Indian Mythology.* Used and adapted with permission of the Thomas Y. Crowell Co., Inc.

To Doubleday & Company, Inc., for "Sun Dancers" by Patricia Irving from *The Whispering Wind Poems* by Terry Allen. Copyright © 1972 by The Institute of American Indian Arts. Reprinted by permission of Doubleday & Company, Inc.

To Field Newspaper Syndicate for the Dennis the Menace® cartoon © by Field Enterprises, Inc.

To Aileen Fisher for "Until We Built a Cabin" by Aileen Fisher, copyright © 1946, copyright renewed 1974. Reprinted by permission of the author.

To Follett Publishing Company for "Papa's Birthday" from *All-Of-A-Kind Family* by Sydney Taylor. Copyright © 1951 by Follett Publishing Company, a division of Follett Corporation. Used by permission.

To Harper & Row, Publishers, Inc., for "Rudolph Is Tired of the City" from *Bronzeville Boys and Girls* by Gwendolyn Brooks. Copyright © 1956 by Gwendolyn Brooks Blakely; and for "Eastern Chipmunks," adapted from *Winter-Sleeping Wildlife* by Will Barker. Copyright © 1958 by Will Barker. By permission of Harper & Row, Publishers, Inc.; and for "Afternoon on a Hill," from *Collected Poems,* Harper & Row. Copyright 1917, 1945 by Edna St. Vincent Millay.

To The Instructor Publications, Inc., for "A Pound Cake for a General" by Treasa Thomas, reprinted from *Instructor,* © 1974 by The Instructor Publications, Inc. Used and adapted by permission.

To Billy Joyce, age 12, Lily Hill Middle School, Philippines, for "Pens," from *Sun Four,* published by the Department of Defense Schools, 1978.

To J. B. Lippincott Company for "A Wish Is Quite a Tiny Thing" from *For Days and Days* by Annette Wynne. Copyright © 1919 by J. B. Lippincott Company. Copyright renewed 1947 by Annette Wynne. Reprinted by permission of J. B. Lippincott Company.

To McGraw-Hill Book Company for "Beach Fire" from *The Little Whistler* by Frances Frost. Copyright © 1949; and for "Voyage to Outer Space" from *Rocket Away!* by Frances Frost. Copyright © 1953 by McGraw-Hill, Inc. Used with permission of McGraw-Hill Book Company.

To Katherine W. Moseley for "The Watermelon Seeds," published in the American Red Cross Youth *News,* March, 1969; used by permission of A. G. Moseley, Jr.

To Plays, Inc., for "The Floating Stone," by C. W. Fould and Doris P. Buck. Reprinted by permission from *100 Plays for Children,* edited by A. S. Burack, Plays, Inc., Publishers. Copyright © 1949, 1970 by Plays, Inc. This play is for reading purposes only. For permission to produce this play, write to Plays, Inc., 8 Arlington St., Boston, MA 02116.

To The Saturday Evening Post Company for "Cold Drinks on the Cuff" by Frances B. Watts. From *Child Life* magazine, copyright © 1974 by The Saturday Evening Post Company; and for "Lucia and the *Americanos*" by Barbara S. Neelands © 1964; "The Prince Said, 'Me First' " by Jo Beth Rice Luttrell © 1966; "Timmy Pretend" by Marjorie Murch Stanley © 1964; "Chuka's Hawk" by Elizabeth B. Whitmore © 1964. All from *Jack and Jill* magazine, © The Curtis Publishing Company. Reprinted by permission of the publisher.

To Scholastic Magazines, Inc., for "A Citizen of Two Countries" by Lavinia Dobler. Reprinted by permission of Scholastic Magazines, Inc., from *News Explorer* magazine. Copyright © 1958 by Scholastic Magazines, Inc.

To Debbie Shumate, age 14, Nile C. Kinnick High School, Japan, for "When I Write a Poem" from *Sun Three,* published by the Department of Defense Dependents Schools—Pacific, 1978.

To Wonder Books for "Indian Messages" by Evelyn Andreas, adapted from *The Cub Scout Book of Cowboys and Indians.* Copyright © 1954 by Wonder Books, a division of Grosset and Dunlap, Inc. By permission of the publisher.

To Vivian G. Zwaik for "Second Chance for King." Used by permission.

Contents

one

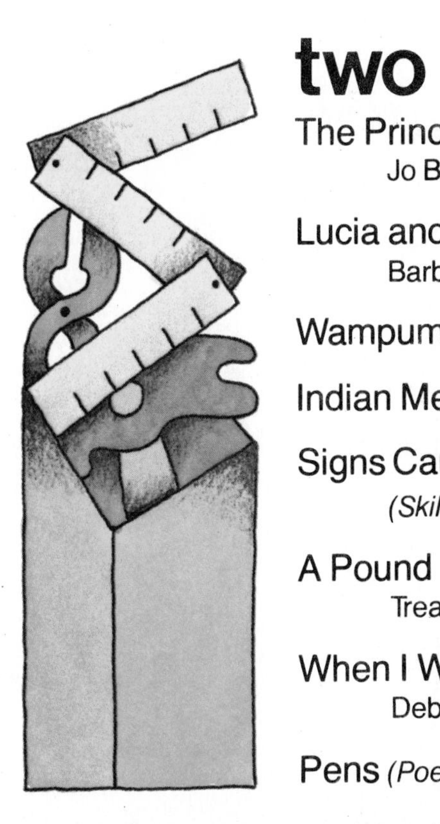

two

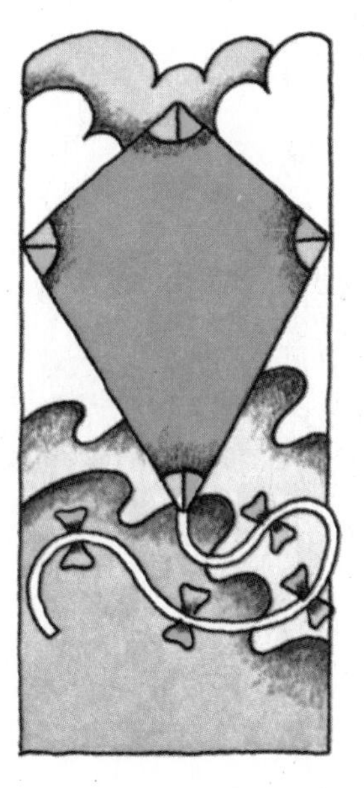

three

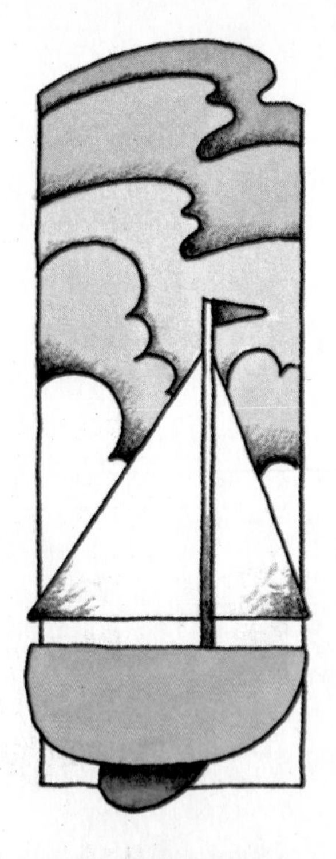

four

five

six

one

Dream Builder

I write a message on the sand
  to the golden fish in the silver sea;
A message that hunters will understand:
  Soon the great fish will belong to me!
For though the fish may ride the waves
  The power of this wish
I cast into the silver sea
  Will catch the golden fish.

Bobbi Katz

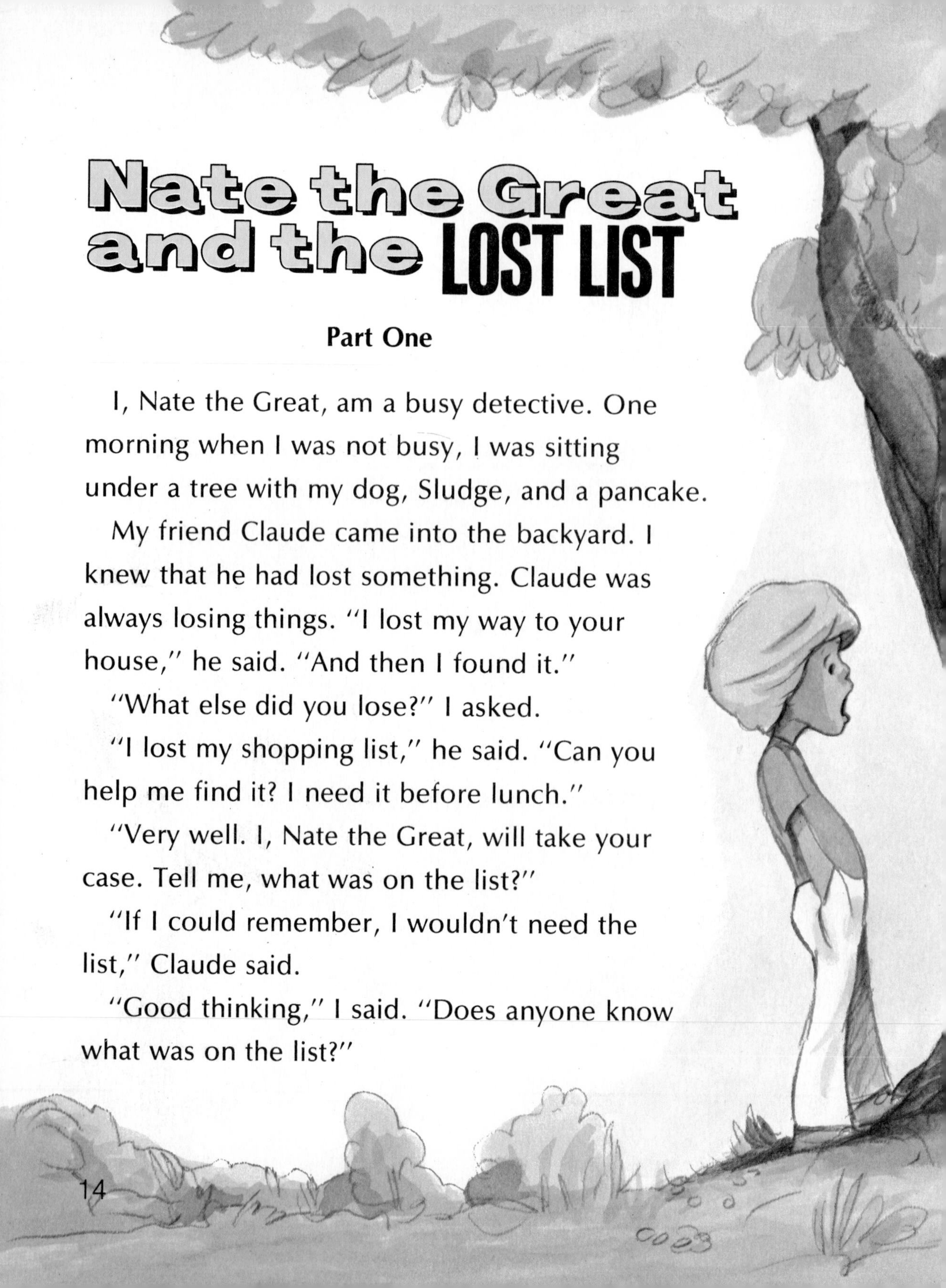

Nate the Great and the LOST LIST

Part One

I, Nate the Great, am a busy detective. One morning when I was not busy, I was sitting under a tree with my dog, Sludge, and a pancake.

My friend Claude came into the backyard. I knew that he had lost something. Claude was always losing things. "I lost my way to your house," he said. "And then I found it."

"What else did you lose?" I asked.

"I lost my shopping list," he said. "Can you help me find it? I need it before lunch."

"Very well. I, Nate the Great, will take your case. Tell me, what was on the list?"

"If I could remember, I wouldn't need the list," Claude said.

"Good thinking," I said. "Does anyone know what was on the list?"

"My father," said Claude. "He wrote it, but he won't be home until lunch."

"Can you remember some of the list?" I asked.

"Yes," Claude said. "I remember salt, milk, butter, flour, and fish."

"Now, tell me, where did you lose the list?" I asked.

"If I knew, I could find it," he said.

"Then I, Nate the Great, know what to do. I will draw a map of every street between your house and the food store, and we will follow the map."

I got two pieces of paper and a pen. I drew a map on one piece of paper and wrote on the other:

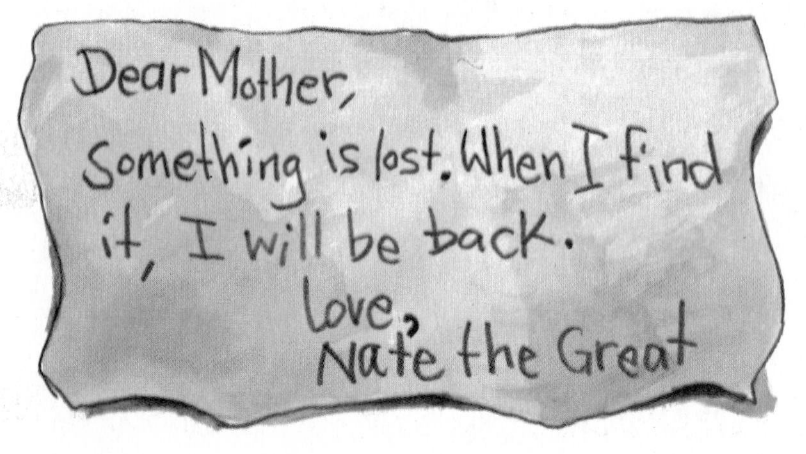
Dear Mother,
Something is lost. When I find it, I will be back.
Love,
Nate the Great

Claude and I walked between his house and the food store and then between the food store and his house. Sludge sniffed. But we could not find the list.

"Maybe it blew away," I said, as I dropped the map to the ground.

"What are you doing?" Claude asked.

"I am dropping the map. Whichever way it goes will show us the way the wind is blowing. Maybe your list blew to the same spot."

The map blew toward Rosamond's house. "I will go to Rosamond's house and ask if she has seen your list," I said.

Sludge and I went to Rosamond's house. Rosamond opened the door. She is a very strange girl, but today she looked more than strange. She was covered with flour. Sludge and I sniffed. Rosamond was making pancakes!

We walked in. Rosamond's four black cats were there, only today they were white, too. "I'm making cat-pancakes for my cats," Rosamond said. "I have a new recipe."

"I would like to taste cat-pancakes," I said.

"You're not a cat," Rosamond said.

"I would like to taste them anyway," I said. "A pancake is a pancake."

Rosamond and I sat down, and I ate a pancake. It tasted like fish, but I ate another. "I am looking for Claude's shopping list," I said. "I think the wind blew it toward your house. Have you seen it?"

"I haven't seen a shopping list," she said. "But I see Annie and her dog, Fang, outside my window, and—"

Part Two

"And what?" I, Nate the Great, asked.

"And Fang has a piece of paper in his mouth. It might be the shopping list," said Rosamond.

I got up. "Thank you for your help and your pancakes," I said.

"I'm having a cat-pancake party this morning," Rosamond said. "I've invited all the cats I know. Can you come?"

"I am not a cat," I said.

"That's what I told you before," she said.

Sludge and I went out to talk to Annie and Fang. I like Annie and try to like Fang. "Hello," I said. "I am looking for Claude's shopping list, and I think Fang has it between his teeth."

"He won't let that paper go," Annie said. "He'll get mad if I pull it out."

"I would not like to see Fang mad," I said. "I, Nate the Great, say that we should keep anybody with such strong teeth happy. Very happy."

This was a puzzle. How could I get the paper out of Fang's mouth? Suddenly I had the answer.

"Sludge," I said. "Bark!"

Sludge barked. He barks funny, but that does not matter. Fang barked back, and the piece of paper dropped from his mouth. I reached for it, but the wind blew it away. I ran after it, followed by Sludge, Fang, and Annie.

When the paper blew against a wall, I caught it. The case was almost over. I looked at the paper and saw that it was my map.

"The list is still lost," I said. "I need more clues." I thanked Annie and Fang for their help and walked back to Claude's house.

"I, Nate the Great, have not found your list," I said. "Can you remember anything else that was written on it?"

"I remember! I remember two more things," Claude said. "I remember eggs and baking powder. Can you find the list before lunch?"

"I hope so," I said. "Come to my house before noon."

Sludge and I walked home slowly. This was a hard case. At home I made myself some pancakes. I mixed eggs, flour, salt, baking powder, milk, butter, and sugar together and cooked them. I ate and thought. I thought about the shopping list. I thought about Rosamond and her cat-pancakes, and I thought about Annie and Fang and the map.

Then I had a big idea. I knew I must go back to Rosamond's house even if I did not want to do that. I did not want to be at a party with Rosamond and all the cats she knew. But I am a detective, so Sludge and I walked quickly to Rosamond's house. I said hello to her and more cats than I could count. "I would like to see your recipe for cat-pancakes," I said.

"Here it is," Rosamond said, handing it to me.

"There are no steps to follow," I said.

"I don't need any," said Rosamond. "I just mix some of everything together."

"Where did you get this recipe?" I asked.

"I found it today," Rosamond said. "I found it near my house."

"I have something to tell you. I, Nate the Great, say that your cat-pancake recipe is Claude's shopping list."

I stood tall and read the recipe. "Salt, milk, butter, flour, eggs, baking powder, sugar, and fish."

"Oh," Rosamond said. "When I found the paper, I thought it was a cat-pancake recipe."

"Yes," I said. "And when I saw Fang holding a piece of paper, I thought it was a shopping list. I thought it was what I hoped it was. When you saw the list, you thought it was what you hoped it was, a cat-pancake recipe. I, Nate the Great, thought of that when I was making pancakes. I mixed eggs, flour, salt, baking powder, milk, butter, and sugar. Some were on Claude's list. The other thing Claude remembered was fish. Cats like fish, so—cat-pancakes!"

"Oh," Rosamond said. "Well, Claude can have his paper back. I'll keep the recipe in my head."

"That is a good place for it," I said. "It cannot blow away."

I said good-by to Rosamond and more cats than I could count. Then Sludge and I went home with the list.

It is now past noon. Here comes Claude. I am glad I do not have to look for him to give him his list. And I am glad the case is over. I, Nate the Great, have something better to do. I, Nate the Great, am going to finish my rest.

THINK ABOUT IT

1. What two things had Claude lost? Which of those things had he found?
2. Who had found Claude's list? What did that person think the list was?
3. Did Claude remember everything on the list? Could he have gone shopping without the list?
4. What was Nate like? What was Claude like? What was Rosamond like?
5. If you had been Nate, would you have tasted the cat-pancakes? Why or why not?

Paul Bunyan and His Day Off

Paul Bunyan was a giant of a man who lived in the North. He had fought more wild animals than any other man. He had also fought more men than any other man. But he fought only when he had to and did not often lose his temper. He was best known for cutting more logs than any other man in the North. In one minute, he could cut a hundred logs.

Paul worked hard cutting logs, so sometimes he liked to take a day off to have fun. On one of the coldest days in the middle of the winter, Paul decided to take a boat ride. He jumped aboard the nearest rowboat and began to row out to sea.

It was so cold that the water turned to ice as he rowed. He rowed harder and harder as the water kept freezing around his boat. He rowed so hard that his heels broke through the floorboards, and he slid into the water below. Before he could climb back up through the broken boards, ice formed over his head.

Paul swam along from one air pocket to another looking for an opening in the ice. Then he tried pushing against the ice with his heels. "Well, I declare," he said to himself. "If I don't find an opening soon, I'll freeze under here."

He swam and thought and swam and thought. "Maybe I can signal for help with my shoe," he decided. He took off a shoe and began to pound on the ice over his head. He pounded and pounded, but no one was around to hear his signal. He pounded so hard that blocks of ice flew a hundred feet high.

At last the hole was large enough so that he could crawl out. He crawled out and up and over the blocks of ice. Then he made his way back to his broken rowboat.

He pulled himself aboard the boat and thought hard. "Well, now," he said to himself. "Maybe I can sail to the nearest island even if the water *is* frozen over."

He took an old blanket from a seat in the boat and hung it from a board. Then he blew and blew. That old boat sailed smoothly over the ice straight for the nearest island. Paul smiled with delight as the boat neared the land.

As soon as the boat touched land, Paul jumped off. He pulled the broken boat onto the shore. "Well, now," he said to himself. "I must find a way to get warm."

He took the blanket from the boat and put it around himself. Then he knelt to build a fire to get even warmer. He used the boards from his boat for the fire because he couldn't cut any logs. He had not remembered to bring his ax along.

Soon the fire gave off a warm glow. Paul smiled with delight to be warm again. "Well, now," he said to himself. "I would be happy but for one thing. I hope I remembered to bring something to eat. I surely am hungry."

Paul looked in all his pockets. In one pocket, he found hundreds of bits of corn. These he threw into the fire. Then he sat there catching the bits of corn as they popped. He ate most of the popcorn.

Some of the corn, however, popped so high that a cloud of popcorn formed in the sky. It wasn't long before that popcorn cloud grew too heavy to hold all the corn. Suddenly the corn rained down on Paul's fire, putting it out. Without the fire, there was no glow. Without the glow, Paul couldn't see, for it was now night. There were no lights on the island.

"Well, now," said Paul to himself. "I need an electric light, but there are no electric lights here on the island."

He thought and thought. Then he remembered an electric light bulb he had been carrying in his pocket. He took it out and reached toward the nearest star. As he touched the bulb to the star, a bright glow spread over the island.

"That's better," he said to himself with delight. "Now I must think of a way to get back home."

As Paul was thinking, the bright hot glow from the light bulb began to melt the ice. Soon there was no ice left. "Now I can't walk home across the ice," he said to himself. "And I don't think I can swim that far. Now, how can I get back?"

Paul thought and thought. As he was thinking, he happened to look down at his jacket, which had nine large shiny buttons. "Well, now, I declare," he said to himself. "These buttons look just like stepping stones."

With that, he pulled the buttons off his jacket. He tossed one button into the water and stepped onto it. Then he tossed another button. He stepped and tossed and stepped and tossed until all nine buttons had been used as stepping stones. From the last button, he took a giant step and was back on land.

Back home again, Paul smiled with delight. "Well, now," he said to himself. "This has been a great day. Now I'm ready to cut logs again."

THINK ABOUT IT

1. What kind of man was Paul Bunyan?
2. One cold day, Paul rowed out to sea. What happened to the water as Paul rowed? What happened to Paul?
3. How did Paul get out from under the ice?
4. How did Paul reach the island?
5. How did Paul keep himself warm? What did he eat? What did he use for light?
6. How did Paul get back home?
7. Could Paul take care of himself—no matter what? Did Paul ever seem to get upset?
8. Could this story really happen? Why or why not?

Until We Built a Cabin

When we lived in a city
(three flights up and down)
I never dreamed how many stars
could show above a town.

When we moved to a village
where lighted streets were few,
I thought I could see ALL the stars,
but, oh, I never knew—

Until we built a cabin
where hills are high and far,
I never knew how many
many
stars there really are!

Aileen Fisher

Afternoon on a Hill

I will be the gladdest thing
Under the sun!
I will touch a hundred flowers
And not pick one.

I will look at cliffs and clouds
With quiet eyes,
Watch the wind bow down the grass,
And the grass rise.

And when lights begin to show
Up from the town,
I will mark which must be mine,
And then start down.

Edna St. Vincent Millay

Pictures That Light Up

Would you like to be able to make your drawings more exciting? Suppose you could add lights to your scenes without using electric lights! It's not magic. It's not even a science experiment. You can do it with only two different colors of paper, scissors, and staples. The following pages explain how. First read all the steps to be sure you understand them. Then you can begin to work.

You will need three sheets of colored paper, 8 inches by 10 inches. Two of the sheets should be dark blue or black. The other sheet should be yellow. Scissors, a white crayon, and staples will also be needed.

1 Take one sheet of dark blue or black paper. With the crayon, draw a scene of a town or city with houses and other buildings. Be sure to have windows and doors in your buildings.

2 Use scissors to cut out all the doors and windows. Cut out a moon in the sky.

3 Place a sheet of yellow paper behind your scene. Make sure all the sides are even.

4. Staple the top and the bottom of the two sheets together. Be sure to staple close to the edge. You must leave enough room to put a strip of paper between these two sheets.

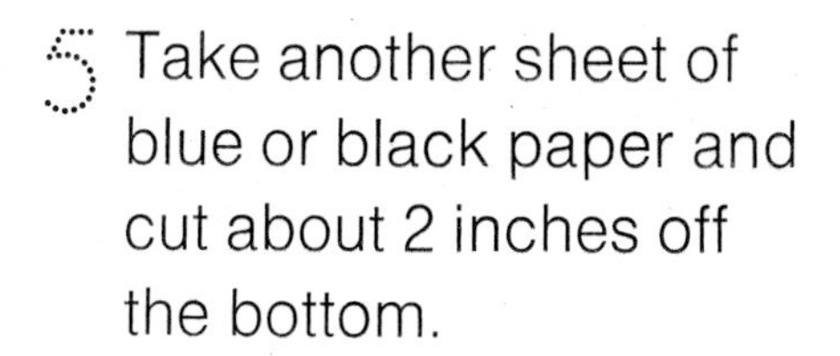

5. Take another sheet of blue or black paper and cut about 2 inches off the bottom.

6. Slide this strip between the two stapled sheets, covering the yellow paper.

7 When you want your scene to look as if the lights are on, slowly pull out the strip. Then you will see yellow lights in the windows and doors, and the moon will seem to be shining.

When you plan to send a card to someone, make one like this. Print your message on the strip, and send it to your friend.

Eastern Chipmunks

Eastern chipmunks are busy little animals. They work, play, and rest at different times of the year. Now and then you can hear the chipmunks make the sound, "Chip!" You might think the name *chipmunk* comes from this sound, but it is taken from an Indian word.

PLANNING AHEAD FOR THE WINTER

When the days are long and the sun is warm, frisky chipmunks gather food for the winter. This is a busy time of year for the eastern chipmunks.

Food Pouches

The chipmunks carry food to their shelters by storing it in two pouches in their mouths. They put some food in the pouch on one side and then fill the other pouch. When both pouches are filled, the chipmunks run off to their tunnel homes to store their food.

Tunnel Homes

A tunnel opening is often hidden. It may be inside an old tree or under a stone wall or hidden under leaves. Young chipmunks dig tunnels that are only 5 feet long. Older chipmunks often dig tunnels that are 20 to 30 feet long. At the end of each tunnel there is a large opening with plenty of room for storing food.

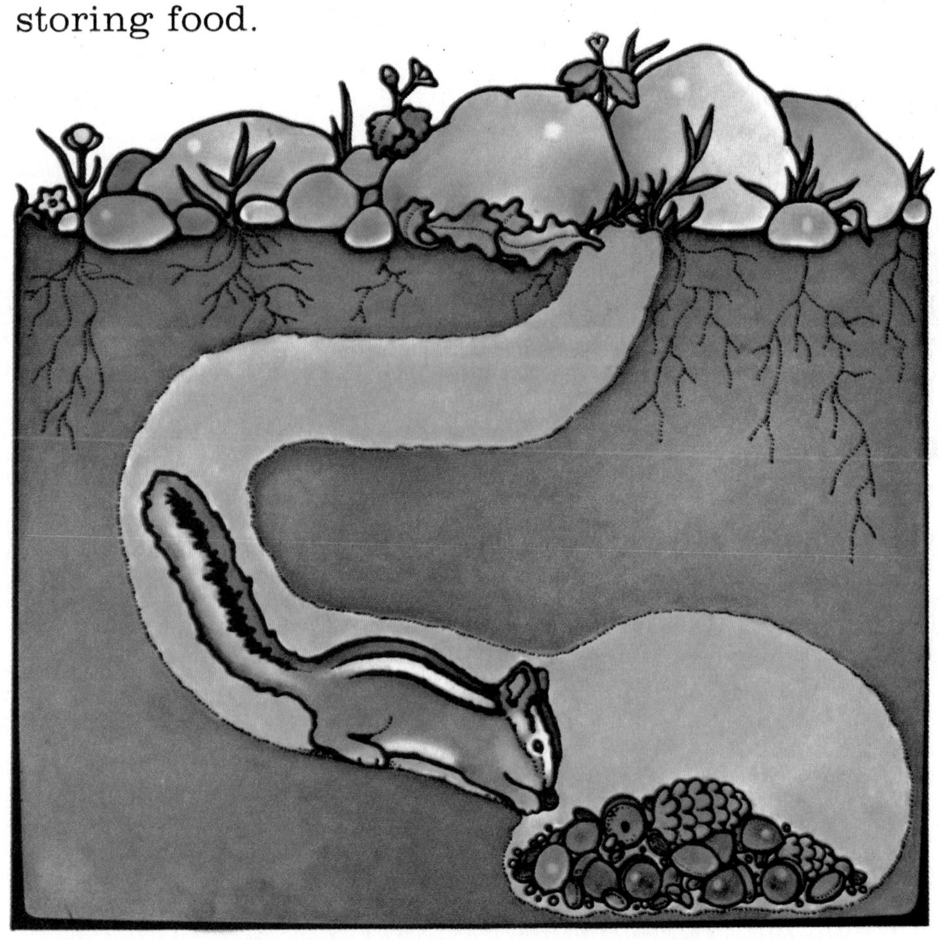

Winter Food

The chipmunks store food under their beds of dried leaves and grass. They sometimes store so much food that their beds reach the top of their tunnels. However, the chipmunks get hungry during the winter. By spring, their beds may be flat on the floor! The chipmunks must work from sunup to sundown to have enough food to store for the winter.

Sleepy Winters

When the first frost is in the air, the chipmunks no longer frisk about looking for food. They stay close to home and eat less and less. Their hearts beat very slowly, and their breathing slows down. The chipmunks get very sleepy and crawl into their shelters to hibernate or sleep away the long winter.

In the northern woods, the chipmunks sleep very soundly. When the days are warmer, the chipmunks wake up from time to time to eat some of their stored food. Chipmunks who live in more southern woods even go outside on warm days.

BREATHING NEW LIFE IN SPRING

The chipmunks hibernate for about five months. When spring is in the air, the frisky chipmunks appear, fresh from their winter rest.

Playtime

When most of the snow is gone and the sun begins to warm the earth, the chipmunks know it is spring. Now, the chipmunks are very playful. They run in and out of holes. Then they rest for a time.

Baby Chipmunks

Soon after their winter sleep, chipmunks begin their families. When new leaves appear on the wild flowers, the young are born. Four or five baby chipmunks are born at one time.

Baby chipmunks grow up in a month. Then they leave home to build their own tunnels and gather their own food supplies. They, too, must now work hard to be ready for winter. Only when it is very hot do they stop their work. Then they go underground to rest where it is safe and cool.

Once again, the eastern chipmunks have worked hard. Once again, they have lined their tunnels with leaves and grass and have gathered and stored food for the winter months ahead. Then safe and warm in their tunnel homes, the chipmunks rest through another winter.

THINK ABOUT IT

1. How does a chipmunk get ready for winter?
2. When does a baby chipmunk begin to gather its own food?
3. How do chipmunks know when to come out of their tunnels?
4. Why must a chipmunk work so hard to gather food for the winter?
5. Would you like to sleep through the winter? Why or why not?
6. What would you do to get ready for a long winter's sleep?

A Wonderful Day to Fly

It's a clear morning. There isn't a cloud in the sky. It's a wonderful day for flying!

You walk to the wall to call your friend Nina. Maybe she would like to go flying, too. You reach out and push a small green button.

A soft voice says, "Ready."

You say, "I want to talk to Nina, please." Then you wait while your phone dials the number for you. Soon the wall lights up. You can see Nina, and she can see you.

Nina likes the idea of going flying. But then she says, "Wait a minute. Isn't today the day our town gets its rain? Let me ask my father."

Nina goes to find her father, a scientist in a big science department. He does experiments with clouds and always knows when rain will fall.

When Nina comes back, she says, "Yes, today is a rain day. But Dad says the rain will end before lunch. I'll fly to your house then."

"OK," you say. The picture of Nina goes away. You say to the phone, "Hang up, please." The phone turns itself off. You go to the window and watch as the clouds roll in. Soon it begins to rain.

At last the rain ends. When Nina knocks on your door, you put on your flying belt and step outside. You and Nina push buttons on your flying belts and rise into the air. You're off for a wonderful time flying!

Maybe you think that none of these things can happen. You're right. They can't happen yet. But by the time you're an adult, you may have a phone like the one in the story. In fact, some phones already can perform in some of the ways that the phone in the story did.

Right now, you could buy a phone that shows a picture. The phone would cost a lot, however, and the picture wouldn't be very large. You could even buy a phone that dials numbers for you. But you couldn't expect it to do that by just speaking to it.

Scientists are working on all these things. It may not be long at all before your phone can perform in all the ways that the one in the story did.

What about knowing when and where rain will fall? Well, that's harder, but scientists are working on that, too. They watch the action and motion of the wind and clouds. Scientists are learning what kinds of clouds give rain and how much rain they give. They are also learning from what direction the wind comes most often.

Clouds and wind often do things scientists don't expect. There is still much to learn about the action of clouds and the motion of wind. But scientists have already shown that they sometimes can make clouds rain. Scientists hope to learn to make clouds that will move in the right direction to make rain where they want it. Then you could call a scientist on your phone and find out if it will rain and for how long. But that's still a long time away!

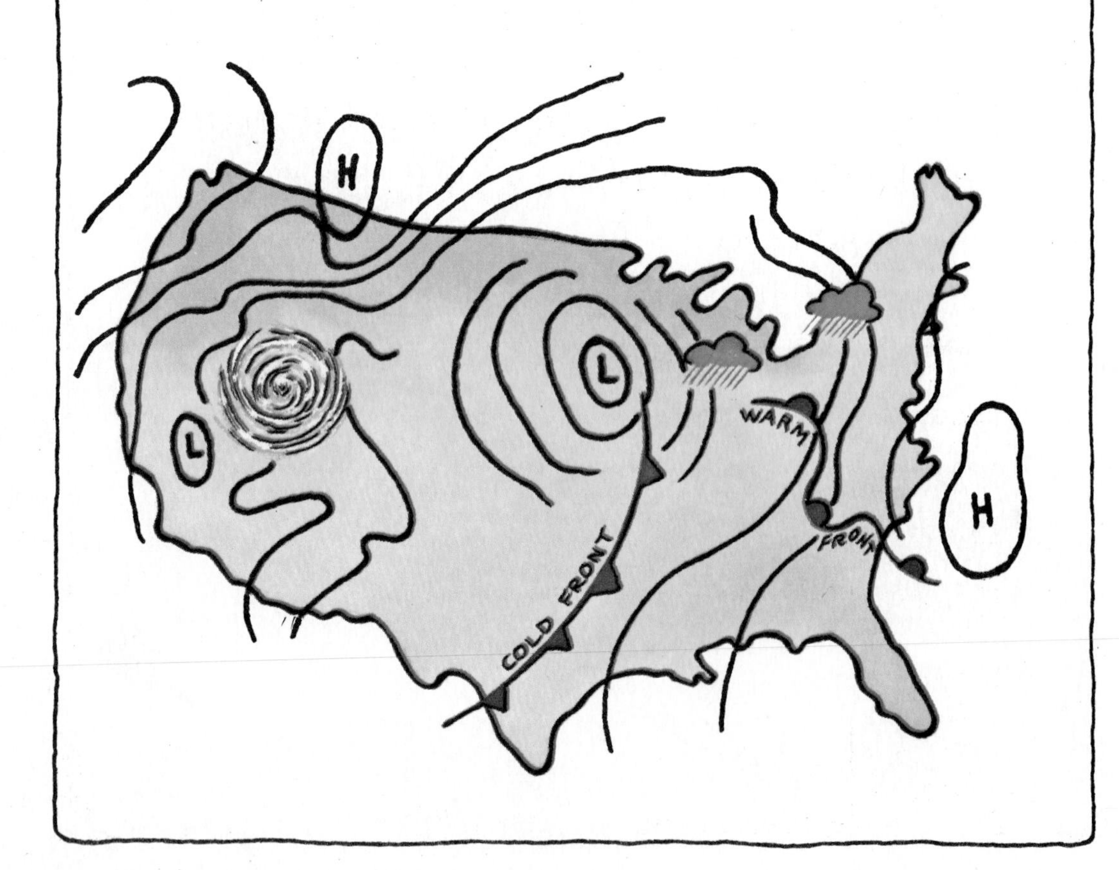

As for one person flying alone, that's a very long time away. It's hard to make a small machine with a strong enough effect to make someone rise into the air and fly. There are some machines now that can help one person fly, but they are quite large.

These machines are heavy, too. They have to lift their own weight and the person's weight into the air. So the machine may shake the person as it rises. Also, it isn't always easy to change direction. The wind may also shake the person around. All these things mean that a flying machine for one person isn't very safe yet. But someday it may be.

Science can't grant every wish people have, but it has brought many wonderful things. In time, scientists may find ways to grant your every wish.

When you are an adult, maybe you will help. You may find a way to make a phone that can hear a person's voice and then follow orders. Maybe you will find a way to make the wind and clouds do as you wish. Or you may find a way to make a small flying machine with a strong enough effect to lift one person.

Someday, you may look outside on a clear day. Then you may call a friend and say, "It's not going to rain today. It's really a wonderful day for flying. Let's go!"

THINK ABOUT IT

1. Right now, could you buy a phone that shows a picture or that dials numbers when you speak to it?
2. Today, could you call a scientist to find out *for certain* when and where rain will fall?
3. Can you buy a machine that would take you flying—all by yourself?
4. Why do you think scientists want to learn more about the action of clouds and the motion of wind?
5. What are some ways that science has helped people?
6. If you could ask a scientist to make something special, what would you ask for?
7. Would you like to be a scientist? Why or why not?

two

THE PRINCE SAID
"ME FIRST"
CHARACTERS
The King
The Queen
The King's Wise People
Prince Richard
Prince Hal
Prince John
A Man with a flute
Knights, Servants, Children, and
Singers and Comics of the court

SETTING: *A castle in a far-off land. The King's knights and wise people have gathered. Everyone is watching the Queen.*

King: Come now, my dear. We are all here ready to help you. What is it that is upsetting you so?

Queen (*Sighing*)**:** Our boys have all been so naughty today! They are not well-behaved anymore at all. No one would think they were royal princes.

King: Now then, now then! Let's hear what they've done.

Queen: Well, first, baby Prince John was naughty. That child seized his pet dragon's tail and pulled until the little dragon cried out.

King: Well, he shouldn't have, of course. But that's only a childish prank.

Queen: Oh? Well, just listen to this childish prank! Prince Richard was even naughtier than Prince John. He scratched pictures on the walls.

King: Dear, dear! He shouldn't have done that!

Queen: And Prince Hal was the naughtiest of all. He wants to be first in everything. He is always shouting, "Me first! Me first!" He thinks no one but himself should ever be first. Oh, dear! Such a selfish child! (*She sighs again.*) I don't know what to do. I'm ready to pull out my royal hair!

King (*Turning to the wise people*): Ladies and gentlemen, you can see what we are up against. You are the wisest people in the land. You must help us. What can we do? How can we teach Prince Hal to behave himself and not be so selfish? (*The wise people sit and think and scratch their heads.*)

Wise People (*Speaking all together*): Too bad, too bad! (*They all think hard.*)

A Young Wise Man: You could give Prince Hal a good spanking—but only by a royal hand, of course.

A Young Wise Woman: No, no, no! A spanking would never do for a prince. (*They all scratch their heads and think again.*)

An Older Wise Man: I have it! To teach the Prince a lesson, let us put a spell on him. For one day he *must* be first at everything. I mean *everything*!

All the Wise People (*Perfectly delighted*): Yes! A perfectly good idea! Good, good! That's what we'll do. (*Everyone shakes hands, and the Queen looks happy.*)

SCENE II

SETTING: *The Eating Hall. The royal family is at the table.*

Prince Richard: I know what we're having to eat. (*Delighted*) Roast duck!

Prince Hal: Roast duck? Terrible! I don't like roast duck.

Prince Richard: I do. I love it.

Prince Hal: I hate it! I can't eat it. And I won't eat it. (*A servant starts to serve the King. Prince Hal begins to shout.*) Me first! Me first!

King: What? For roast duck? (*He motions to the surprised servant, who then places the serving of duck before Prince Hal. The Prince begins to eat.*)

Prince Richard: I thought you hated duck.

Prince Hal: I do. It's terrible. It's the most terrible dish there is. (*He goes right on eating.*) I hate roast duck!

Prince Richard: Then why are you eating it? That's just foolish if you ask me. You're eating it as if you loved it!

Prince Hal: I can't help it. I don't want it, but something is *making* me eat it! (*The King and the Queen look at each other. Prince Hal eats all the duck on his dish. Then he runs out of the Eating Hall.*)

SCENE III

SETTING: *The castle gardens, where some servants are standing by a pool.*

Prince Hal: Look at that dirty pool full of mud. What an ugly green color it is!

Prince Richard: The servants have got to clean it this afternoon.

Prince Hal: I wouldn't want that job. I wouldn't go near that pool.

Prince Richard: Look, they're about to step into the pool and get to work.

Prince Hal: Oh! Me first! Me first! (*He seizes a servant's broom, jumps into the mud, and begins to clean the pool.*)

Prince Richard (*Calling*): I thought you didn't want that job!

Prince Hal: I don't! I don't! I don't want to be here at all. This is all so foolish! (*But he goes right on cleaning the pool until it shines. At last he climbs out, covered with mud.*)

Prince Hal: I'm so tired. I want to go to bed. I just want to sleep. (*He drags himself along. Then some children come running up to him, followed by a man playing a flute.*)

Man: Who wants to dance? Who will dance to my merry music? (*He begins to play, and the children start to dance.*)

Prince Hal: Me first! Me first! Me first! (*His feet begin to dance him all over the gardens. Up and down, side to side, round and round he dances.*)

Prince Richard (*Watching in surprise*)**:** I thought you were so tired!

Prince Hal (*Ready to cry*)**:** I am! I am! I wish I had never, ever said those terrible, foolish words! I wish I had never behaved that way. Oh, why have I been so selfish? Why didn't I know that not even a prince should always be first! (*Suddenly, his feet stop dancing. He smiles. He feels much better and happier. The wise people's spell is done!*)

SETTING: *The Great Music Hall, that very night. All the King's knights and wise people are there. Comics and singers have come to make them merry. The royal family appears. Prince Hal hurries to find a chair—for his mother. Everyone smiles.*

Prince Hal (*Smiling*)**:** Won't you be seated first, Mother? (*He does not seem so childish now.*)

Queen (*Surprised*)**:** Thank you, my dear. Well, I know I am the *happiest* mother in the world.

King (*Proudly*)**:** This is indeed a special night. To the wise people, the Queen and I give thanks. Comics, make us laugh! Singers, give us a song! Let us all be merry. (*Then he and the Queen look at the Princes with delight. The wise people wink.*)

THINK ABOUT IT

1. Why did the Queen think that Prince Hal was selfish?
2. What was the first thing that Prince Hal did under the spell?
3. Why did the King and Queen ask the wise people to help them only with Prince Hal?
4. Did the wise people have to think very hard to find a way to teach Prince Hal to behave? Why or why not?
5. Why do you think Prince Hal always wanted to be first?
6. If you had a selfish brother, how would you act toward him?

Lucia and the Americanos

After lunch Lucia Sanchez ran to her spotted pony. Swallow was the nearest thing to a friend she had. Sometimes he seemed almost like a person.

"Let's go see those *Americanos*," she said softly into Swallow's ear. "But we won't get too close to their camp. Father said not to go near strangers. He says some strangers are not honest."

Lucia took the road that led in a northern direction along the foothills. Her own green land stretched out below her as she and Swallow climbed the rocky way. Now and then a little animal jumped through the brush.

At last she spotted the campfire. Beside it stood two covered wagons. She could see people there and—was that a girl near the campfire?

Suddenly she heard a *rattlesnake*! As long as she heard the rattle, she knew that awful snake was not going to strike. Before the rattle stopped, she must take Swallow out of reach of the snake!

She felt her pony move. He, too, knew the danger. Then she looked down and saw his foot. It was caught in a hole between two rocks.

Lucia thought fast. How could they be saved? She could jump off the pony's back away from the snake. But she would never leave Swallow.

Suddenly, the rattle stopped.

"He is ready now," thought Lucia. "He is ready to strike!"

A rifle shot rang out!

Lucia looked down. The awful snake lay still. Lucia threw her arms around her pony's neck. "There, Swallow, it's all right now," she said over and over into his ear. "We are not in danger now."

"Hi!"

The word was English. A boy not much older than Lucia was climbing down from a rocky point above her. A long rifle was in his hand, but his smile was friendly. Lucia smiled back.

"I'll need help," he said, looking at Swallow's foot. Again the words sounded strange, but his meaning was clear. The boy pointed to the wagons, back to Swallow's leg, then at himself. Then he ran off down the hill to the wagons.

Lucia, one arm still around her pony, watched him. "Is he someone who is not honest?" she wondered.

Soon he came back with a tall, thin man.

"Buenos días," the man said slowly in Spanish. "I am Mr. Bell. This is my friend, Jim Miller."

"Good morning. I am Lucia Sanchez," Lucia said in Spanish. Then she remembered to say thank you for the help she had received. *"Gracias, Señor."*

Together Jim and Mr. Bell got Swallow's foot out of the hole. Then Mr. Bell looked at the pony's scratched leg.

"These scratches ought to be dressed," he declared. "Come along and have dinner with us at our camp, Lucia, while I see to your pony."

Lucia followed them down the hill. "Are you an *Americano?*" she asked Mr. Bell.

"Yes," said Mr. Bell, "but my parents came from Ireland many years ago, so I'm Irish, too. I've lived in the Southwest for a time. That's where I learned to speak Spanish."

"Señor," Lucia asked, "are you looking for gold here?"

Mr. Bell laughed. "Not *all* the *Americanos* are looking for gold. No, I'm looking for land to farm. I'm a farmer."

"So," Lucia thought, "the *Americanos* could be farmers like Father, and they could be nice."

She felt really happy when the girl she had seen standing by the campfire came to meet her.

"Hi! I'm Jim's sister. My name is Sally," she said in English, pointing to herself.

Lucia understood. She spoke very slowly. "Hi, Sally." They were the first words of English she had ever spoken. Sally laughed.

Suddenly Lucia jumped up. The sun was high overhead. "I must go home," she cried. "No one knows where I am!"

Mr. Bell shook his head. "You can't ride this pony for a few days," he said. He spoke to the others in English, then to Lucia again in Spanish. "We will take you home in a wagon," he said.

Meanwhile, the men at the ranch had started to search for Lucia. Now, as they were going back to the ranch, they saw the wagon nearing the gate.

Lucia's father saw the wagon, too. "The *Americanos* will never walk inside my ranch," he thought.

Then he saw that the pony beside the wagon was Swallow. He saw Lucia slip down from the wagon seat and run toward him.

Lucia threw herself into her father's arms. "The *Americanos* saved Swallow from an awful rattlesnake!" she cried. "They brought me home. They are honest people who want to farm, and they're nice!"

As soon as her father understood what had happened, he went to meet the strangers.

"*Gracias.* We thank you for saving Lucia and Swallow," he said. "Come into my house."

That evening Mr. Bell and the Millers stayed on the ranch. Lucia showed Jim and Sally the hide shed, the sheep pens, and the ponies. After dinner, there were games and singing.

"Why, I like the *Americanos,*" Lucia thought. Later, as her mother was saying good night, Lucia said, "The *Americanos* are really very nice, aren't they?"

"Yes," her mother said. "The *Americanos* are very nice. Your father thinks so, too!"

THINK ABOUT IT

1. Why did Lucia think that the *Americanos* might not be honest?
2. Why was it good that Mr. Bell could speak Spanish?
3. What do you think Sally and Lucia could learn from each other?
4. Do you think Lucia would have ever met the *Americanos* if she had not been in trouble? Why or why not?

WAMPUM TRINKETS

SUPPLIES

You will need the following:

colored construction paper
scissors
a drinking straw or pencil
glue
a needle and thread
some wool

Created by Dr. John Lidstone, Queens College of the City University of New York, Consultant in Art Education.

American Indians used wampum beads for many things. They made fancy belts, necklaces, and other trinkets from these beads. You can make fancy wampum trinkets, too.

1

Choose a color pattern for your trinket, such as two yellows, one blue, two yellows, one blue. To make a necklace, cut out 2-inch square sections from sheets of construction paper that match your color pattern.

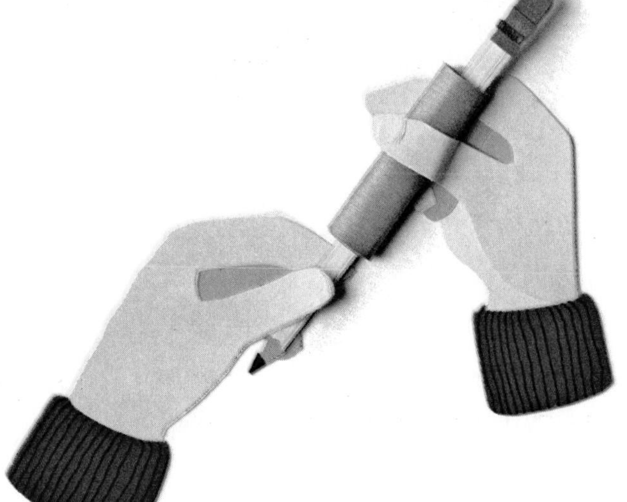

2

Roll a square of paper tightly around a drinking straw or pencil. Glue down the end so that the paper won't open out. Hold the rolled paper tightly until the glue is dry. Then slip it off the straw or pencil.

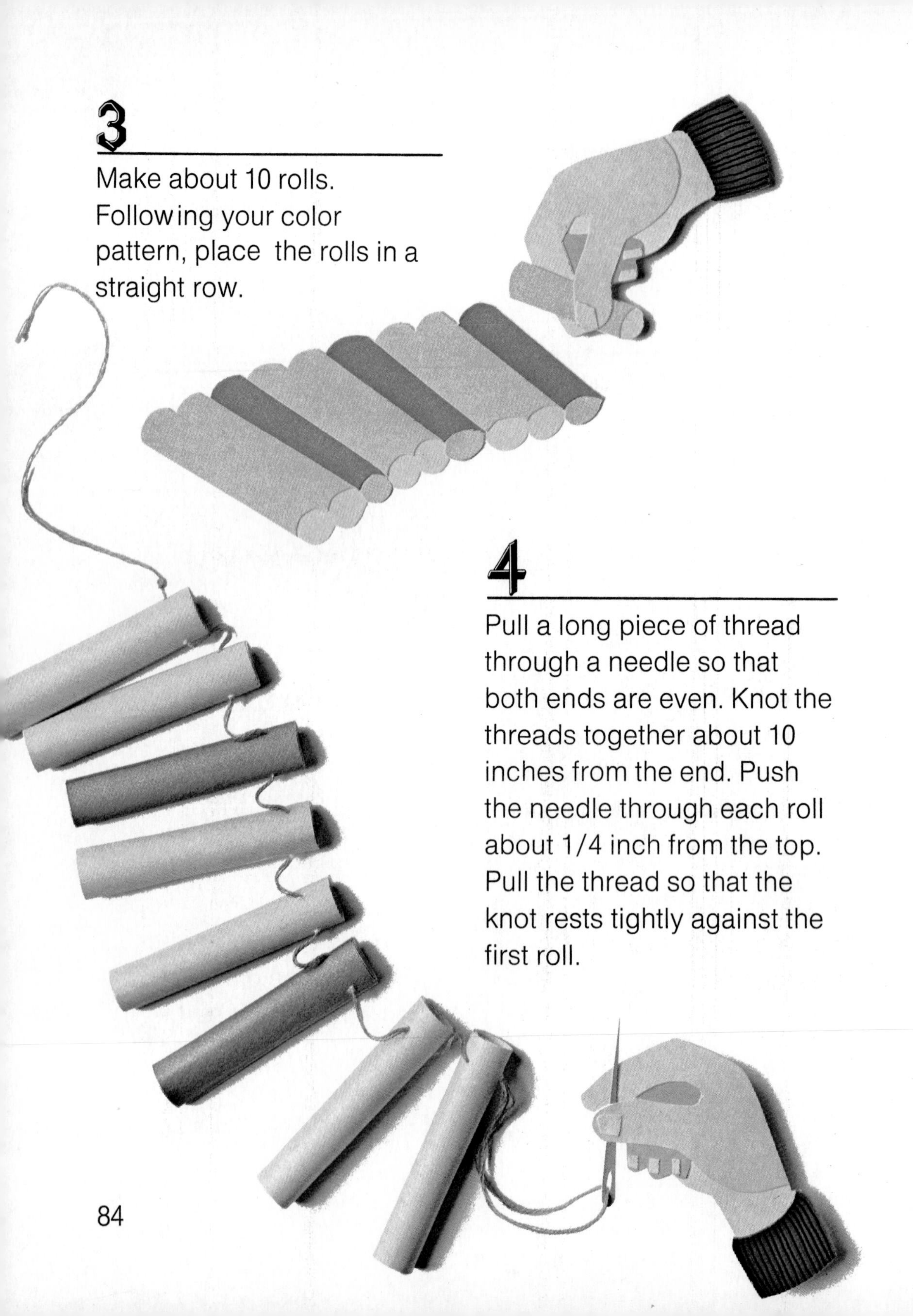

3

Make about 10 rolls. Following your color pattern, place the rolls in a straight row.

4

Pull a long piece of thread through a needle so that both ends are even. Knot the threads together about 10 inches from the end. Push the needle through each roll about 1/4 inch from the top. Pull the thread so that the knot rests tightly against the first roll.

5

Then push the needle through all the rolls 1/4 inch from the bottom. Make a knot tight up against the first roll and leave a 10-inch tail section.

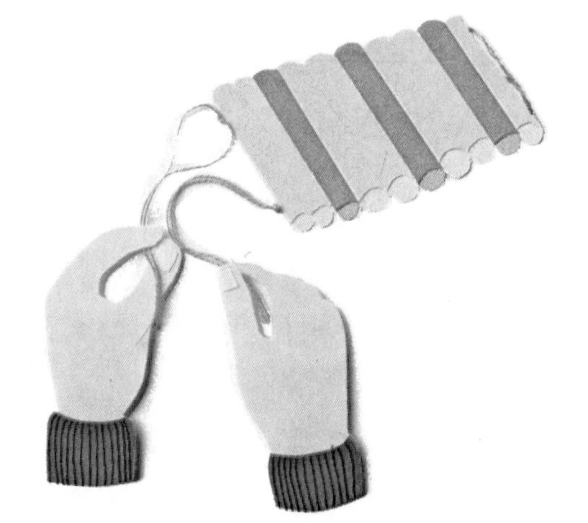

6

To wear your necklace, tie the thread tails to each other.

7

You may add wool, thread, or anything else to make your wampum beads look even fancier.

INDIAN Messages

When you want to get in touch with friends, you can talk to them on the telephone. You can also write them a letter. But sending a message was not always as easy as it is today.

There were no telephones out on the trails for American Indians to use. The Indians could, however, send and receive messages. They did so by using signs and signals and pictures.

Travel Signs

American Indians sometimes used sticks as travel signs. If one group wanted to tell another group where they had gone, they would place sticks in the form of an arrow to tell their direction. Then they would place other sticks to tell how long they would be gone.

1. Two short sticks placed at the end of a long stick would point to the direction the people had taken.

2. Short sticks placed across the long stick would tell how many days the people would be gone. In the picture below, the short sticks tell that the Indians would be gone for four days.

Smoke Signals

American Indians also sent signals with smoke. First, they made a small fire. Then they threw some grass over it to make it smoke. When the fire was smoking, the Indians held their blankets over the smoke. By moving the blankets up and down, they could make the smoke go up in long or short puffs.

All the people of the tribe knew the meaning of the different puffs of smoke. Some of the puffs were danger or warning signals. Some called a council meeting. Others called the tribes together for war. Still others told of peace.

Picture Writing

Besides signs and signals, American Indians often used pictures to tell stories of what they had done.

Some of the pictures they drew showed how brave they were in war. Others showed them dancing around a campfire or bringing home a deer or other animal from a hunting trip.

A Picture Letter

Once an American Indian from Rawhide Peak sent a picture letter to some traders in a post nearby. He painted the pictures on a tanned deer hide. First he drew a picture of an Indian with a mule. Then he drew other things. Can you "read" the letter?

Although the traders could not speak the same language as the Indian from Rawhide Peak, they could understand the letter. They knew that he wanted a pack mule, a roll of red wool, and some seed and corn. The traders kept this letter to show to their grandchildren.

Decorated Objects

American Indians liked to put pictures on just about everything. They decorated their belts, tents, and other goods. Sometimes you can almost "read" their decorations. Here are pictures of some decorated objects.

Keeper of the Wampum

In each tribe of the Iroquois League, there was a chief who was called Keeper of the Wampum. He kept the facts of the tribe.

Wampum was the Indian name for beads made of shell. The beads were put into a belt or sash. Wampum was used for sending messages and also as money.

When one tribe wanted to talk to another tribe about making peace, the Indians would "talk" by stringing their words into wampum. Then they would give their sashes to each other saying, "This belt protects my words." Today, agreements are protected, or made safe, by words written on paper.

Every year on a certain day, wampum belts were brought out at a big council meeting. The Keeper of the Wampum would hold up a belt and say, "With this belt, I open your ears that you may hear."

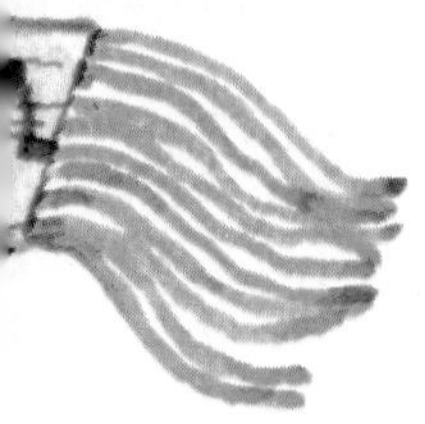

The next time you pick up the telephone or write a letter, think about the ways American Indians sent messages.

THINK ABOUT IT

1. How did the American Indians send and receive messages?
2. How did the American Indians use sticks as travel signs?
3. What did puffs of smoke sometimes signal?
4. What was *wampum?* What was it used for?
5. Instead of wampum, what do we use today to protect agreements?
6. What did the Indians sometimes do when they wanted something from a trader who did not speak their language?
7. How would you send a message to someone who did not speak your language?

Signs Can Help

In "Indian Messages" on pages 86-93, you saw how American Indians used different symbols to send messages. Every day you see symbols that send you messages. Let's think about some of those symbols.

Look at the picture at the left. What special job is the girl doing here? How do you know?

The girl is, of course, helping other children cross the street. If you look closely, you can see her special belt and badge. These are symbols of her job. What do the belt and the badge stand for? What do they tell you about the girl and her job?

Now cover the picture of the girl with your hand. What color is the sign she is holding? How many sides does the sign have—four sides or more than four sides?

Most stop signs are red and white and have eight sides. If you see a stop sign often enough, you know that it means *Stop!* without reading the word.

Look at the signs and symbols below. None of them have words. How many can you read even though there are no words?

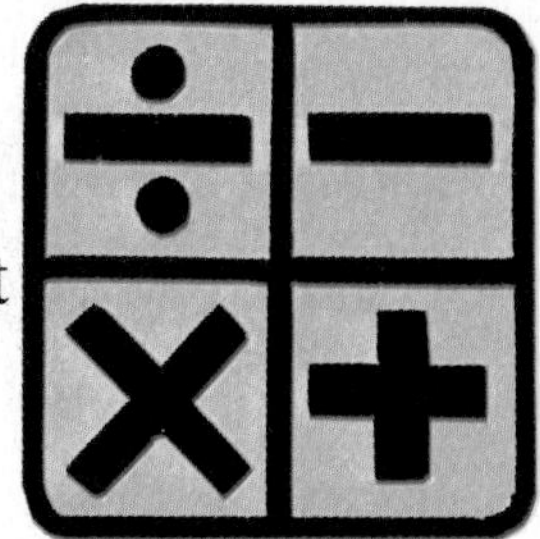

Which of the other books that you use in school uses a great many symbols? If you don't know, look at the clues at the right. Talk in class about the symbols in your math book.

A Pound Cake for a General

From the Morgans' house in Boston, Charlotte could see all the British ships. "Enemy ships!" she thought. The war between the British soldiers and the Americans under General Washington would soon begin. How Charlotte longed for the war to be won by Washington's army!

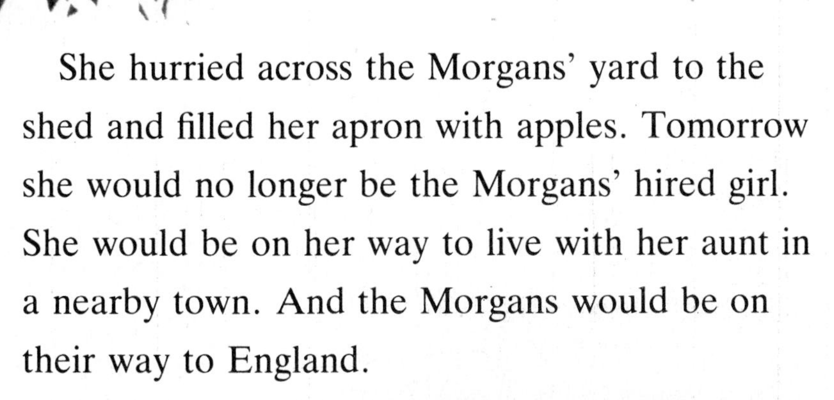

She hurried across the Morgans' yard to the shed and filled her apron with apples. Tomorrow she would no longer be the Morgans' hired girl. She would be on her way to live with her aunt in a nearby town. And the Morgans would be on their way to England.

The Morgans did not believe in this American Revolution against the British. They believed in the King of England, still. Charlotte could never agree with them about that. She was a Patriot and believed in the American cause.

As she started to leave the shed, a man came rushing toward her and placed his hand over her mouth. She heard shouting close by.

"Are you a Patriot?" the man asked. Charlotte nodded her head yes. The man let her go.

"Listen!" he said. "They're going to catch me. If you're a Patriot, you'll want to help." He pressed a little packet of paper into her hand.

"Find a Patriot to deliver this to General Washington at his headquarters in Cambridge. Now scream," he ordered. "The British mustn't suspect you."

Charlotte screamed. British soldiers rushed into the shed and dragged the man away. Charlotte hid the packet deep under the apples. Mrs. Morgan came running to Charlotte.

A British officer stepped out front and Charlotte's eyes opened wide with fear. This man was Captain Kingsley, a friend of the Morgans. He knew Charlotte was a Patriot!

The Captain bowed to Mrs. Morgan. "I am sorry to trouble you, but we caught this Patriot hiding in your shed. My men are searching to be sure he hasn't hidden something there."

"Nothing there, sir," a soldier called.

The Captain's eyes jumped from the man to Charlotte. She was sure that he suspected something. She could see it in his eyes as he stared at her.

"What's in your apron, young lady?"

"Why—apples, sir."

Mrs. Morgan agreed. "We are packing the last of our food now, Captain," she said. "We leave for England tomorrow, you know."

The Captain smiled and bowed. But even so, Charlotte knew that he suspected her.

Safe inside the house, she took the packet from her apron and hid it in her cap. It was small enough to fit in her closed hand. So small—but so important! She must get it to General Washington somehow.

But how? How? All of her father's friends had left Boston, gone off with Washington's army.

Could she deliver the message herself? After all, she was going to Cambridge tomorrow to meet her aunt. Surely no one would suspect *her* as the enemy.

"I'll do it!" she decided.

The next morning as Charlotte and Mrs. Morgan were getting ready to leave, there was a loud knock on the door. It was Captain Kingsley!

"I don't have time to talk now, Captain," said Mrs. Morgan. "I must see that Charlotte is on her way before I leave."

"Certainly, Mrs. Morgan," the Captain said. "If you like, I can travel with the young lady."

Mrs. Morgan was pleased. "You are very kind, Captain." Then she turned to Charlotte. "Hurry, now. Get your things, and don't forget the pound cake for your aunt."

Charlotte hurried to the kitchen. What was she to do now? If the Captain should have her searched, he would surely find the packet.

Quickly, she took the little packet from her cap and pushed it into the bottom of the cake. Then she tied some paper around the cake.

Suddenly the Captain came into the kitchen. He seemed to be staring at the cake.

Charlotte held it out to him. "Would you mind carrying this cake, sir? It's very special."

"Certainly," he said.

It was hard saying good-by to kind Mrs. Morgan. It was harder still, Charlotte decided, to sit in the coach with the Captain. How terrible to travel with a British officer who suspects you!

They drove a short way without speaking. Suddenly Captain Kingsley ordered, "Now then, young lady! I think you have a message given you by the man we caught in Mrs. Morgan's shed. Give it to me!"

Charlotte swallowed hard. "I have nothing to give you," she said. It was true, too. The Captain was holding the pound cake himself. She could see that he did not believe her.

"You may search my bag, sir, if you wish."

He put down the pound cake and opened the bag. He found nothing, much to her relief.

They neared the last post where people could leave Boston. Charlotte held her breath. How could she wait another minute?

"Take off your cap, please!"

She jumped at the sound of his voice. "Yes, sir," she answered quickly.

The Captain watched as Charlotte took off her cap, turning it inside out for him to see.

"All right," he growled.

The coach reached the post. The Captain helped her down. He handed her the pound cake, and Charlotte's heart beat fast.

"Maybe I was wrong this time," the Captain said, "but I always do my job as I see it."

"Yes, sir. Of course," Charlotte said. "Thank you for riding with me all this way."

"You'll find the Cambridge coach just ahead, there at the next post." He pointed out the way.

Charlotte knew, then, that Washington's army was not far away. Her heart sang with relief. Soon she could deliver the message to General Washington.

She never knew just what that important message had said, but it had brought good luck to the Americans. The British withdrew from Boston before long. Then a letter came to Charlotte from General Washington himself. It said, "I am sure that with the help of brave Patriots like you, this war will be won."

THINK ABOUT IT

1. What did Charlotte mean when she called herself a Patriot?
2. Was Charlotte honest when she told the Captain that she had nothing to give him?
3. Although Charlotte was a Patriot, how did she feel about Mrs. Morgan?
4. Why did Charlotte ask the Captain to hold the pound cake?
5. Would Charlotte make a good soldier? Why or why not?
6. If you were Charlotte, would you be willing to deliver a message another time? Why or why not?

When I Write a Poem

When I write a poem,
I like it to rhyme,
And then I feel the work
is mine.

When I write a poem,
I like to see,
things expressed by me, me,
me.

When I write a poem,
I like to look,
At something that's mine
and not right out of a book.

Debbie Shumate

Pens

Pens show my feelings.
They express my thoughts for me.
They respond to me.

Billy Joyce

three

TIMMY PRETEND

Timmy was playing a pretend game of baseball with two teams of little toy players. Mother and Father were pasting photos in the family album. Timmy's big sister, Katherine, came into the room with a model plane kit that she preferred to work on.

"Watch out!" Timmy shouted to Katherine. "Don't move. There's a mouse!"

"Where?" asked Mother, dropping her scissors onto the album.

"Where?" asked Father, dropping his tube of paste.

"Where?" shouted Katherine, dropping her model plane kit on a chair.

"There!" Timmy pointed to the floor by the chair.

Father tiptoed over to the chair and picked up a piece of gray yarn. Father shook his head and looked at Timmy. "Were you just pretending?" asked Father, holding the yarn.

"No," answered Timmy. "It looked like a mouse's tail going under the chair."

"Little Timmy Pretend," said Mother, picking up the scissors and the tube of paste.

Katherine was cross. "Little Timmy Tricks is more like it. He thinks he's being funny," she said, picking up her plane kit.

Timmy felt sad. No one believed him. "It looked like a mouse's tail," Timmy said again to himself.

"Last night you thought you saw a huge water bug," said Father. "And you knew there was no water bug. Timmy, I'm tired of your tricks."

"The night before, you thought you saw a spider," said Mother. "And there was no spider. Timmy, you really must stop pretending."

"And now tonight you thought you saw a mouse," said Katherine. "Timmy, maybe there's something wrong with your eyes!"

"I'm not pretending," Timmy said. "I'm not playing tricks. I really thought I saw a water bug. I really thought I saw a big black spider. I really thought I saw a mouse's tail."

Timmy was very sad. No one believed him. Katherine looked at Mother. Mother looked at Father. Father looked at Timmy.

Mother said, "Do you think . . .?"

Father said, "Could it be . . .?"

Katherine said, "The doctor would know."

"But I'm not sick," said Timmy. "Really I'm not sick."

"Not that kind of doctor," Mother told him. "The eye doctor. Maybe you need glasses."

"No, no!" cried Timmy. "I want to be a baseball player. I can't play ball if I have to wear glasses."

"You can't play ball if you can't *see* the ball," Father said. "Besides, wearing glasses won't prevent you from playing ball. It will *help* you."

The very next day the eye doctor looked at Timmy's eyes. "This boy needs glasses," the doctor said.

In a few days the glasses were ready, and Timmy put them on. "I can see much better," said Timmy. "With the special safety glass, I am even able to play baseball."

That very night Timmy was playing his pretend baseball game in the middle of the floor. He looked up and saw something, but he didn't shout. He preferred not to upset anyone this time. Then Timmy saw the same thing *moving*. So he said quietly, "I see something moving on top of the shelf. Look at the shelf!"

“Don’t start that again,” said Mother, going on with her reading.

Father did not say anything. He decided to wait and see this time.

“Up to your old tricks!” said Katherine.

“No, I’m not,” cried Timmy. “I’m wearing my new glasses! This time it’s a real mouse, and it’s getting ready to jump. Look behind you!”

“It is a real mouse,” cried Mother. “We must do something.” She grabbed her sweater from the back of her chair and threw it over the mouse.

The mouse squirmed free from under the sweater. Mother couldn't prevent the mouse from getting away.

"I'll catch it," said Katherine. But the mouse ran past her too quickly.

"I'll take care of this," said Father, tiptoeing toward the mouse. He grabbed an empty can to catch it in. But he, too, could not prevent the mouse from getting away.

Timmy was standing by the front door as the mouse ran toward him. "Right this way," said Timmy, opening the door. The mouse ran out of the house.

"Well, Timmy, that was quick thinking," Father said, putting an arm around Timmy. "You're some hero!"

"No Timmy Pretend this time," said Mother, kissing his cheek. "You're a real Timmy Hero."

Katherine wasn't cross anymore. "*That* Timmy Trick worked fine," she said, patting his head.

"I really am glad I have glasses," Timmy said. "Now you will believe me when I say I see something. I could see where that mouse was every minute."

"If you can see a mouse," said Father, "think how clearly you'll be able to see the baseball you are getting for your birthday tomorrow."

"But my birthday isn't until next week," said Timmy.

"Are you sure, Timmy Hero?" asked Mother.

Timmy ran to the calendar. "My birthday *is* tomorrow!" he cried. "Without my glasses, I was looking at the wrong week."

"Look in the hall closet," Father told him.

Timmy looked in the closet. He saw a ball, a bat, and a catcher's mitt. Then he saw a funny thing that looked like a cage. He put it on his head right over his safety glasses and went back into the living room.

"We hope you'll have a very happy birthday, Timmy," the family said.

"I am sure I will!" Timmy said. He could see their smiling faces as clear as anything.

THINK ABOUT IT

1. Why was Timmy called "Little Timmy Tricks"?
2. Why didn't Timmy want to wear glasses?
3. With his glasses on, Timmy said that he saw a mouse. Why didn't his father say anything?
4. How could the eye doctor have made Timmy feel better about getting glasses?
5. Do you think that Timmy will play better baseball as "Timmy Hero"? Why or why not?

THE BEAVER EXPERT

"Beavers! All you beavers, over here, please!"

Jenny was in the forest near the pond when the voice reached her. Walking through the trees, she came out of the forest near a tent she had never seen before. Suddenly she heard the voice again.

"Wake up and get out of those lodges!"

Jenny turned around to see a tall man calling out orders over the still pond.

"What are you doing?" she asked him.

"I'm trying to get all the beavers together," he answered.

"I kind of guessed that," said Jenny. "Why?"

"I'm Jim Gray," he said. "And I am a beaver expert. I'm here to teach these beavers how to be better builders."

"I'm Jenny. What do the beavers need to know that they don't already know?" Jenny asked.

"Well, they can learn to work faster and save time and wood," Jim explained. "You see, I plan to train some beavers. Then I'll hire them out to builders. My beavers could save builders lots of money."

Jenny didn't really want to hear any more. "I'll see you around," she said. And, shaking her head, Jenny went home.

Jim didn't even see Jenny go, because by now a number of beavers were standing around him.

"Glad you beavers could join me this morning," said Jim, smiling.

"Make it fast," called one female. "We worked all night, and now we want to get some sleep."

When Jim saw her sleepy mate's sharp teeth, he started talking fast. He told the beavers they could make stronger dams by mixing real cement with their mud. Then he explained a better way to cut notches in tree trunks. Soon Jim shared his ideas on how to roll tree trunks into the pond and how to dive faster. Most of the beavers agreed that Jim had some good ideas.

So the beavers did what Jim told them to do for two days. But things didn't work out.

"How am I going to get this ugly white cement out from between my lovely yellowish teeth?" Emma wanted to know.

"My tail hurts from those fast dives," cried a male named Gordon.

"My upper lip hurts from trying to cut bigger notches," sniffed another male, Max.

"Three big tree trunks almost rolled over me," said Max's mate, Sally. "And I don't think that's at all funny."

In fact, only the frogs who lived around the pond thought Jim's ideas were funny. The frogs laughed for hours watching the beavers try their new tricks. But the beavers didn't share the laugh.

"I've had enough of this," Emma said to Sally and Max on the third day.

"I'm with you, Emma," Max nodded. "But I don't think this expert is prepared to give up."

Max was right. The beaver expert did not give up. He told one beaver how to be a faster swimmer and another how to join sticks to have a lodge built faster. But the fight didn't start until Jim tried to tell Max how to fix his upper lip.

"My lip hurts because I listened to you in the first place," shouted Max as he stamped his furry little foot. "Don't tell me what to do anymore. Go be an expert at some other pond."

Jim was wondering about what Max had said when Jenny came by. She wanted to see how Jim was doing. Jim told her about his troubles.

"I think I have to get away awhile from this pond," sighed Jim.

"I'm going home for lunch. Why not come with me?" Jenny asked.

Jenny prepared lunch as soon as they got to her house.

"Here you are," Jenny said.

"What's that?" cried Jim, looking at the yellowish mess Jenny put in front of him.

"That's fish, cheese, and milk mixed together," smiled Jenny. "This is the fast way to eat. Just swallow this and lunch is over."

"I get the picture," whispered Jim. "Thanks."

Awhile later, Jim called all the beavers together. He said, "I want to tell you all that I'm sorry. I've learned that the fastest way to do something is not always the best way. Tomorrow morning I'll be leaving. I hope you won't have trouble getting things back to the way they were."

The beavers were quiet. In a strange way, they would be sorry to see Jim go.

"Just a minute," called Emma. At last she had got the cement out of her mouth using a sharp twig. "We're sorry, too."

"For what?" growled Max, ready to fight.

"For not saying thanks for all the good things he showed us," said Emma to Max. Looking at Jim, Emma went on. "The cement was not a good idea. But Max's notches are much better than before."

"What?" shouted Max.

"Quiet, or you'll hurt your upper lip again," whispered Gordon. In a louder voice, Gordon said, "Now lots of us can dive better."

"And," called a female beaver, "thanks to you, I'm a faster swimmer."

"So, you see," said Emma, "you're not a bad beaver expert after all."

Jim smiled happily.

"Even," added Emma, smiling, "if you do have white teeth."

THINK ABOUT IT

1. Why did Jim Gray call the beavers together?
2. What were some of the things that Jim Gray thought the beavers should learn?
3. What happened to Emma's lovely yellowish teeth?
4. What happened to Max's upper lip?
5. What lesson did Jenny teach Jim Gray?
6. How did the beavers feel at first about what Jim Gray was trying to do? How did they feel at the end of the story?
7. Have you ever tried to make someone do something *your* way? What happened?

Donna Finds a Way

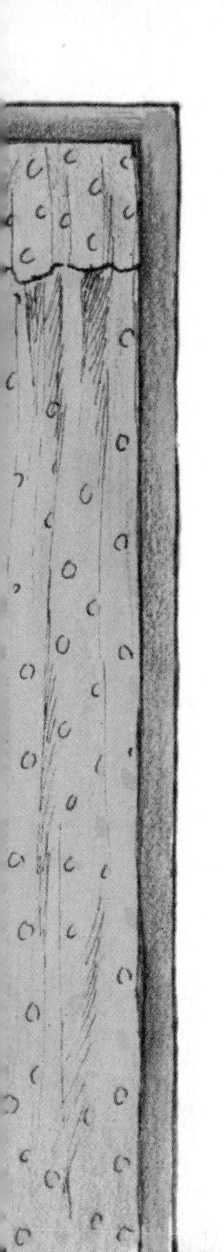

Donna Leonard raced out the front door and jumped on her bike. She heard the door slam shut behind her as she rode off. The bike wheels kicked up pebbles as she hurried off for her singing lesson.

Donna had been taking singing lessons twice a week for a year. She was now learning songs from an opera and loved them. Her teacher, Mrs. Silver, told her that she was learning to sing them very well.

At today's lesson, Mrs. Silver handed Donna a new song. Donna studied it for several minutes. It was harder than any of the other songs she had learned. "Do you really think I can learn this?" she asked.

"I know you can learn it," Mrs. Silver answered. "If you're ready, let's start."

Donna nodded excitedly. She rose to her feet and began to sing.

When the lesson was over, Donna rode home, humming happily all the way. The first thing she heard when she opened the front door was her brother Steve playing the accordion. As she passed the living room, she peeked in. Steve was busily pushing buttons as he played.

Mrs. Leonard was in the kitchen. She looked worried but smiled at Donna. "Would you set the table, please, Donna?" was all she said.

Donna nodded and began to set the table. She wondered if something was wrong. Then she forgot about everything but her new song.

Dinner that night was quiet. No one said much. When everyone was through eating, Steve stood up to clear the table. Mr. Leonard shook his head and said, "No, sit down, Steve. I have something to tell you both. I'm afraid that you're going to have to give up your music lessons. For the past six months, the restaurant has been losing money. Until more money comes in, we have no money for music lessons."

Steve didn't say a word. But Donna cried angrily, "I can't stop my lessons now! Mrs. Silver just told me how well I'm doing!"

Mr. and Mrs. Leonard looked sad. Mrs. Leonard said gently, "I'm sorry, Donna. We know how much your singing means to you. But we're going to need you at home after school from now on. I have to work more hours in the restaurant."

Steve said, "Look, Donna, I'll play your songs for you so that you can learn them."

Donna tried to laugh but began to cry instead. "I couldn't hear myself sing over that noisemaker of yours," she said, as she ran from the room.

The next day, Mrs. Leonard was already at the restaurant when Donna got home. Steve was playing his accordion but stopped when Donna came in. "I've been waiting for you," he said. "I think I can play softly enough for you to sing along. Let's work together."

"Oh, all right," said Donna. She found her sheet music and handed it to Steve. After studying the music, he began to play.

When he was finished, Donna said excitedly, "That sounded great!" Steve played the song again, and Donna sang along.

After that, they played and sang every day. Steve learned all the songs Donna knew, and then they learned more songs together. They had such fun!

But every night, their parents came home from the restaurant looking worried. At last, Donna asked, "Dad, is the restaurant still losing money?"

Mr. Leonard sighed. "Yes," he said sadly.

"Maybe there's a way I can help," said Donna.

Mr. Leonard smiled at her. "I don't think so, but thank you anyway," he said.

"Even if I'm just a kid, there must be something I can do to help," Donna said.

"No, dear," said Mr. Leonard. "We've a big feast coming up next week, and there's no way you can help with that."

Donna went outside. She let the door slam behind her. Angrily, she kicked a pebble. "There must be *something* I can do, even if I *am* only a kid," she said to herself. "I can do lots of different things."

Suddenly Donna had an idea. She ran back into the house to find Steve. "Listen," she said. "I've thought of something we can do to help our parents. Why don't we perform at the restaurant? Then maybe people will come to hear us, and our parents will make more money."

"What makes you think people would want to listen to us?" asked Steve. "They wouldn't want to hear opera songs in a restaurant."

"We can learn other songs," said Donna. "Dad says there's a feast coming up next week. We could learn songs to go with the feast."

"You know," said Steve, "your idea might work. Let's try."

"I'll find some music," Donna said happily. She ran to her room and came back with some songs. When their parents came home, Steve and Donna were busily playing and singing their new music.

All that week, Steve and Donna learned the new songs. At last, they knew them perfectly. That night, Donna said, "Mom and Dad, Steve and I want you to listen to something. Please sit down in the living room."

Mr. and Mrs. Leonard sat down. Steve began to play one of the new songs, and Donna sang along. When they were finished, their parents were quiet for a minute. Then Mrs. Leonard said proudly, "That was wonderful! You two are really very good!"

Dad laughed and said, "So you learned to sing with that noisemaker after all, Donna!"

Donna laughed too. Then she looked at her father and said, "Steve and I want to play and sing in the restaurant for the feast."

Mr. and Mrs. Leonard looked at each other and smiled. Then they said, "All right."

"Oh, thank you!" cried Donna excitedly.

The next day, Steve and Donna went to the restaurant to set up the loudspeaker. Then they watched the people coming in for the feast. "The crowd seems noisy," whispered Donna. "Do you think one loudspeaker will be enough?"

"We'll find out," said Steve, as Mr. Leonard led them to the center of the room.

As they began to perform, the people became quiet. At the end of the first song, everyone cheered and called for more songs.

The next night, they performed again. More people came into the restaurant. At the end of each song, the cheers were so noisy that Steve and Donna could hardly hear anything else.

The feast lasted for one week. At the end of the week, Mr. Leonard said, "At last we're making money again. People really like music while they're eating. Soon you should be able to start your music lessons again. And how would you like to perform twice a week?"

Donna and Steve smiled at each other. "Of course," Donna said proudly. "We're glad that we can help!"

THINK ABOUT IT

1. Why did Donna and her brother Steve have to give up their music lessons?
2. What did Steve think that he and Donna should do? Did Donna agree?
3. How did Donna and Steve help their parents make more money?
4. How did Donna feel at first about having to give up her lessons? How did Steve feel? How did Mr. and Mrs. Leonard feel?
5. Do you think that Donna's idea to perform in the restaurant was a good one? Why or why not?
6. Have you ever had to give up something that you liked doing? How did you feel? How did you act?

A Wish Is Quite a Tiny Thing

A wish is quite a tiny thing,
Just like a bird upon the wing.
It flies away all fancy free
And lights upon a house or tree.
It flies across the farthest air
And builds a safe nest anywhere.

Annette Wynne

Texture Prints

You have seen designs printed in your books. Did you know you could print a design yourself? All you need are potatoes and sponges. By printing with more than one object, you can show different textures in one design. Using more than one color will also add to your design.

Before you begin work, read the directions carefully. Be sure you understand what to do. If you have any questions, ask your teacher.

To make a printing, you will need drawing paper, paints, a dish, a black crayon, cut potatoes, and small pieces of sponge.

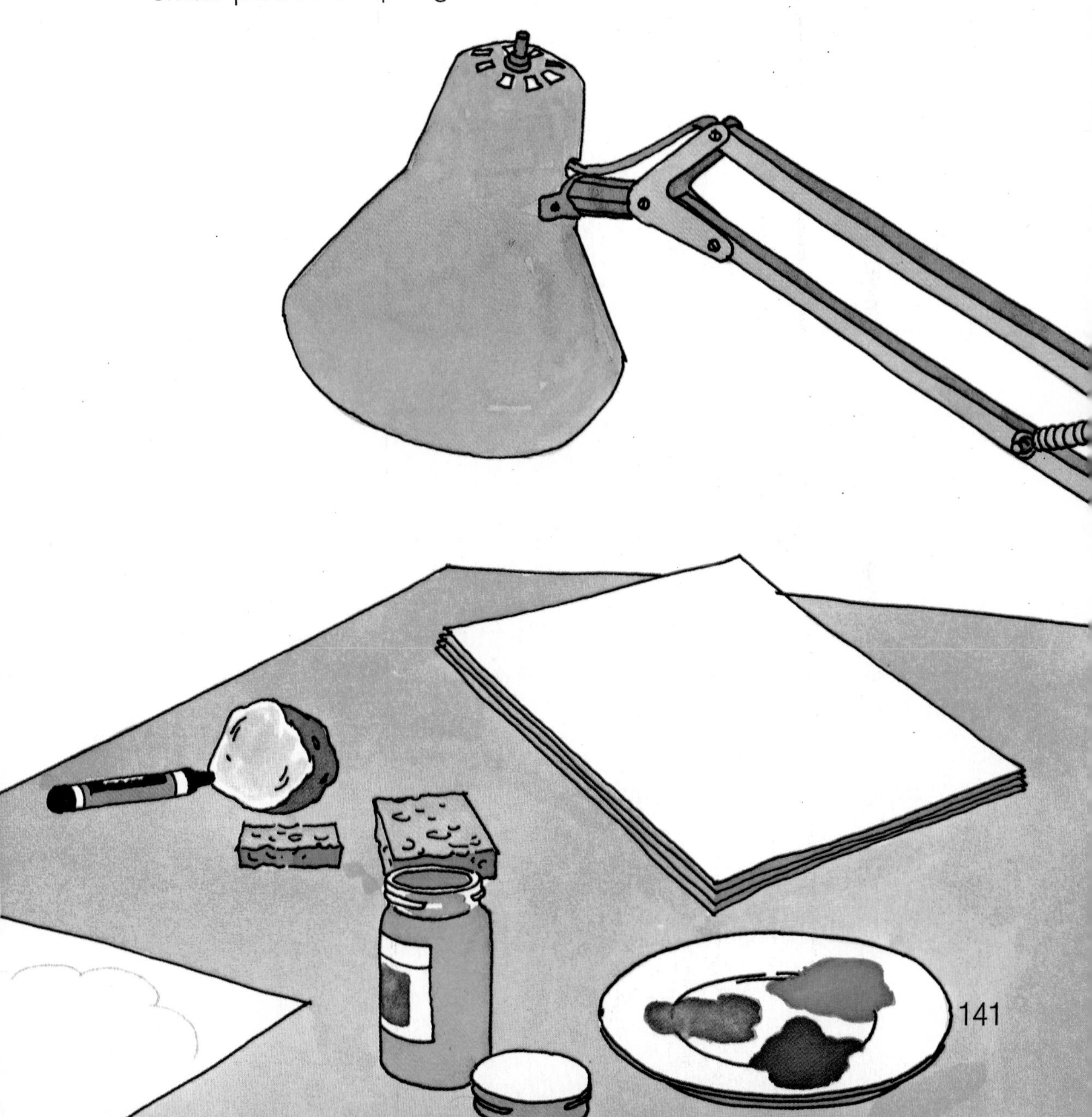

Decide on a shape, and draw it on your paper. Some ideas might be a tree, a flower, or an animal. To print, dip the potato or sponge in paint. Then press on your design. Repeat until you fill in the shape.

Try to use both the potato and the sponge to show different textures. If you use more than one color, use a different piece of potato or sponge for each.

Allow your printing to dry. Then decorate it with a black crayon.

You could use a potato or sponge print to make place mats, cards, or book covers.

COME ONE, COME ALL

Cold Drinks on the Cuff

In just three weeks the Benders were going to the beach. Jane needed a rubber raft to ride the waves. She had not been careful with last summer's raft. She had left it outside, and the Dugans' dog had taken a bite out of it. So this year Mother said that Jane would have to buy a new one herself.

A raft costs seven dollars. Jane had saved up three dollars in her bank and needed four more dollars. She decided that selling cold drinks would be the fastest way to earn the money.

One Friday afternoon, Jane made up signs that said:

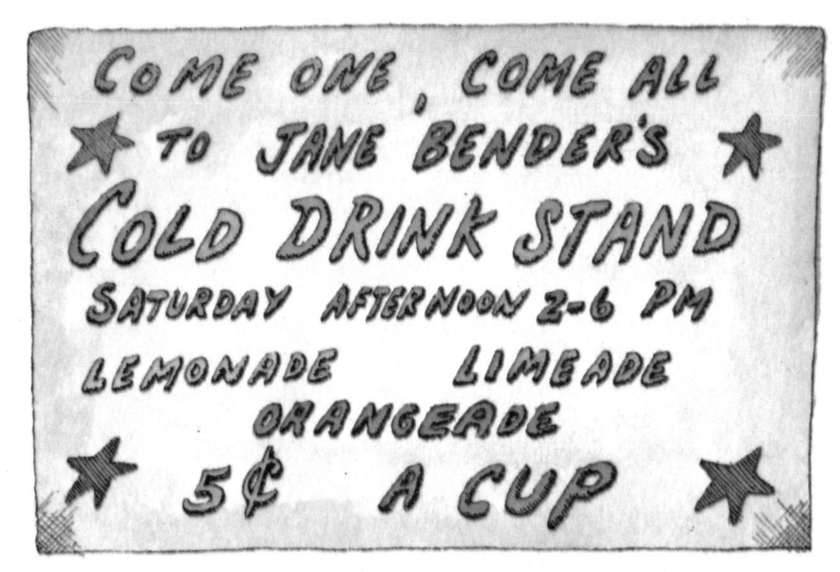

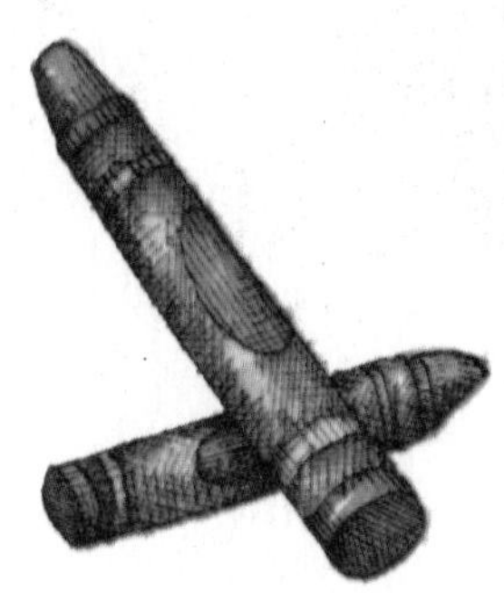

Early Saturday morning, Jane hung the signs about town where people would be sure to see them. Then she spent her whole month's allowance on lemons, limes, oranges, and paper cups. By a quarter of two, the cold drink stand was ready. It was set up under the Benders' window on the sidewalk. On a card table, Jane had spread a flowery paper covering. Then she had stacked up cups and set three pitchers filled with the cold drinks noted in the signs.

Luckily, the day was a warm one. By four o'clock that afternoon Jane had sold four orangeades, five lemonades, and one limeade to different customers.

Then Bobby Clute came over to the stand. This customer really made Jane happy. She was delighted to see him, for Bobby could outeat and outdrink anybody on the block.

"I'll take one cup of each, Jane," said Bobby.

Happily, Jane poured three drinks into paper cups. Then she held out her hand for the money.

"Just put it on the cuff, please," Bobby said.

"On the cuff?" Jane repeated with a question.

COME ONE
TO JANE
COLD
SATURDAY
LEMONADE
ORANGE
5¢ A CUP

"It means 'charge it'—until Monday, that is," explained Bobby. "I get my allowance on Mondays."

"Well, all right," Jane agreed.

Before long, Jane had put eleven more cold drinks on the cuff for Bobby Clute. She was a little worried about it. But she decided that putting a total of seventy cents on the cuff for Bobby made good sense. Why, he was by far her best customer!

Jane's plan for a cold drink stand turned out well. She earned a total of $3.35 in cash. When Bobby paid his bill, she would have just enough money for the raft, with five cents left over.

Then Monday came and went, with no sign of Bobby. On Tuesday Jane found him on the steps of his building.

"Bobby! Where's that seventy cents you owe me?" she asked.

"You should have collected from me yesterday while I still had my allowance," he said. "I've spent it already on milk shakes."

"But you promised!" said Jane.

"Well," said Bobby, "you'll just have to wait until next Monday." He turned away.

Jane began to feel angry. "I'll be back to collect my money," she promised him.

The next Monday morning Jane raced over to the Clutes' house. She found Bobby sitting on the steps again. He was eating chocolate doughnuts.

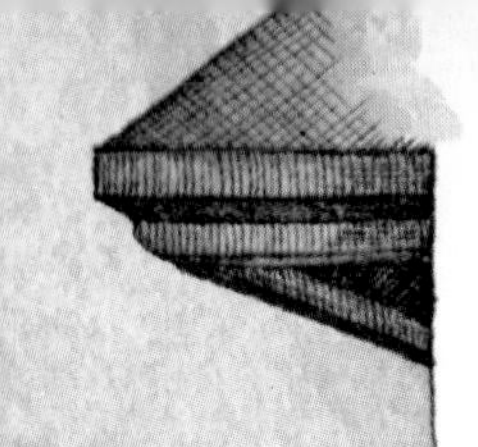

"Hi," Jane said. "Where's my seventy cents?"

"Spent it," answered Bobby, holding up a chocolate doughnut. "You didn't get over here early enough. The early bird catches the worm, you know!" Bobby laughed.

Jane stomped angrily home to plan how she could collect the money next Monday. Time was growing short. She had to have that raft, but it seemed clear that Bobby was trying to outsmart her. If he could keep spending his allowance before she could collect, he might never pay up. That was what Bobby had in mind. But before the day ended, Jane had a plan of her own.

Early the next Monday morning Jane went to find Bobby. This time she did not find him in front of his house. "Maybe I've come early enough to catch him *before* he has spent his allowance," she thought to herself.

Jane waited for Bobby on the sidewalk. Just then, Mr. Clute came through the front door of the building. "Hello, Jane. What are you doing here?" he asked.

"I'm waiting here for Bobby," said Jane. "Did I get here in time?"

Mr. Clute looked puzzled. "Well," he said, "I'm not sure just what you mean. But Bobby should be out soon. I just gave him his allowance, and he's planning to go downtown."

"That's what I thought," said Jane.

Mr. Clute hurried off to work. In a few minutes, Bobby stepped out the front door. He tiptoed down the steps. Suddenly, he looked straight ahead and spotted Jane.

"Oh, no!" cried Bobby. "It's you! What are you doing here so early?"

"I wanted to catch you while you still had your allowance money," said Jane. "The early bird catches the worm, you know."

Bobby was caught. This time Jane had outsmarted him. Sadly, he handed her the seventy cents he owed her.

"Thank you," she said. "The next time I have a cold drink stand, there will be no more charging on the cuff. We'll be better friends that way."

Bobby nodded. He had only a nickel left. It was not nearly enough for a trip downtown.

It was Jane who went shopping that day. She bought a strong raft with a green cover.

THINK ABOUT IT

1. How did Jane plan to save money to buy a raft?
2. What does "put it on the cuff" mean?
3. What did Jane have to do to sell cold drinks?
4. Why did Jane have to pay for the new raft?
5. How might the saying "The early bird catches the worm" have given Jane her idea?
6. What did Jane learn about letting friends "charge it"?
7. Would you like to be friends with Bobby? Why or why not?
8. How would you save money for something you wanted?

Keep Track

Suppose that Jane, the girl in "Cold Drinks on the Cuff," decided to keep on selling cold drinks. Here is one way that Jane could keep track of the number of drinks she sold.

COLD DRINKS SOLD

DAY	NUMBER OF DRINKS
Monday	
Tuesday	
Wednesday	
Thursday	
Friday	
Saturday	

= 6 lemonades = 6 orangeades = 6 limeades

You just read a special kind of graph. Where on the graph did Jane write the names of the days of the week? What picture did Jane use to show the number of lemonades that she sold? The number of orangeades? The number of limeades? Where did she tell us the number that each picture stands for? Can we say that each picture is a symbol for the number 6?

Look at the graph again. Next to Tuesday, there are two lemons and two oranges. The two lemons mean that 2×6, or 12 lemonades, were sold on Tuesday. What do the two oranges next to Tuesday mean? Were any limeades sold on Tuesday?

Graphs use symbols to show facts in a way that is clear and easy to understand. Read the rest of Jane's graph to find out the following facts.

1. On which day did Jane sell the most drinks?
2. On Wednesday, did she sell more lemonades or more limeades?
3. How many drinks did Jane sell in all?

Make a graph of your own in which you show how many girls and boys there are in your class. Draw and letter the graph as shown below. Think of a symbol for a girl and a boy. Draw the symbols on the graph.

GIRLS AND BOYS IN MY CLASS

Row	Number of Girls and Boys

four

The Land Under-the-Sea

Many, many years ago, a young man named Urashima Taro lived in a village in Japan. He made his home with his parents in a hut near the sea. Every morning he went out in his fishing boat. Every evening he came back with a net full of fish.

One evening, Taro saw two boys throwing sticks at a tortoise on the beach. He became very angry at this unkind act. "Let that tortoise go back to the sea," he said. "Otherwise it will die."

"We didn't mean to hurt it," said one of the boys. "We were just having some fun."

The boys gave Taro the tortoise and ran off down the beach. Taro gently put the tortoise back into the sea and watched it swim away.

The next day, Taro was out in his fishing boat. Suddenly he heard a voice calling, "Taro! Taro!" The voice seemed to come from the sea.

Taro leaned over the side of the boat. There in the water was the tortoise.

"I came to thank you for saving my life," said the tortoise. "If you wish, I will take you to the castle in the Land Under-the-Sea."

"We have heard of the Land Under-the-Sea," said Taro. "But no one has ever been there. I for one cannot swim that far."

"You do not have to swim," said the tortoise. "I will take you on my back."

So Taro jumped on the tortoise's back and held on tight. Down, down, down they went into the amazing Land Under-the-Sea. Taro was busy looking at everything. The water was blue like the sky. There were seaweeds as big as trees. Fish of every color swam above his head.

At last the tortoise said, "There is the castle."

"Oh!" said Taro. "Look at the gold roof. Look at the sand, shining like jewels."

When the tortoise swam up on the beach near the castle, Taro stepped down onto the sand.

"Welcome to my castle," said a tall young woman who suddenly stood where the tortoise had been. She wore a sea-green robe made of jewels. "I am Nara, the ruler of the Land Under-the-Sea. I have brought you here because you saved me from those unkind boys."

"No, I didn't," said Taro with a puzzled look. "It was a tortoise that I saved."

"You are right," said the woman, smiling. "I changed into a tortoise and went up, up to the Land Above-the-Sea. I do that now and then. Most people there are unkind to me, but you were kind. I brought you back here to stay forever."

"I cannot stay here forever," said Taro. "My parents would miss me."

With a smile, Nara led her guest to the garden. There they ate dinner from dishes made of silver shells.

After dinner they visited the different parts of the garden. In the eastern part of the garden, it was always spring with cherry trees in bloom.

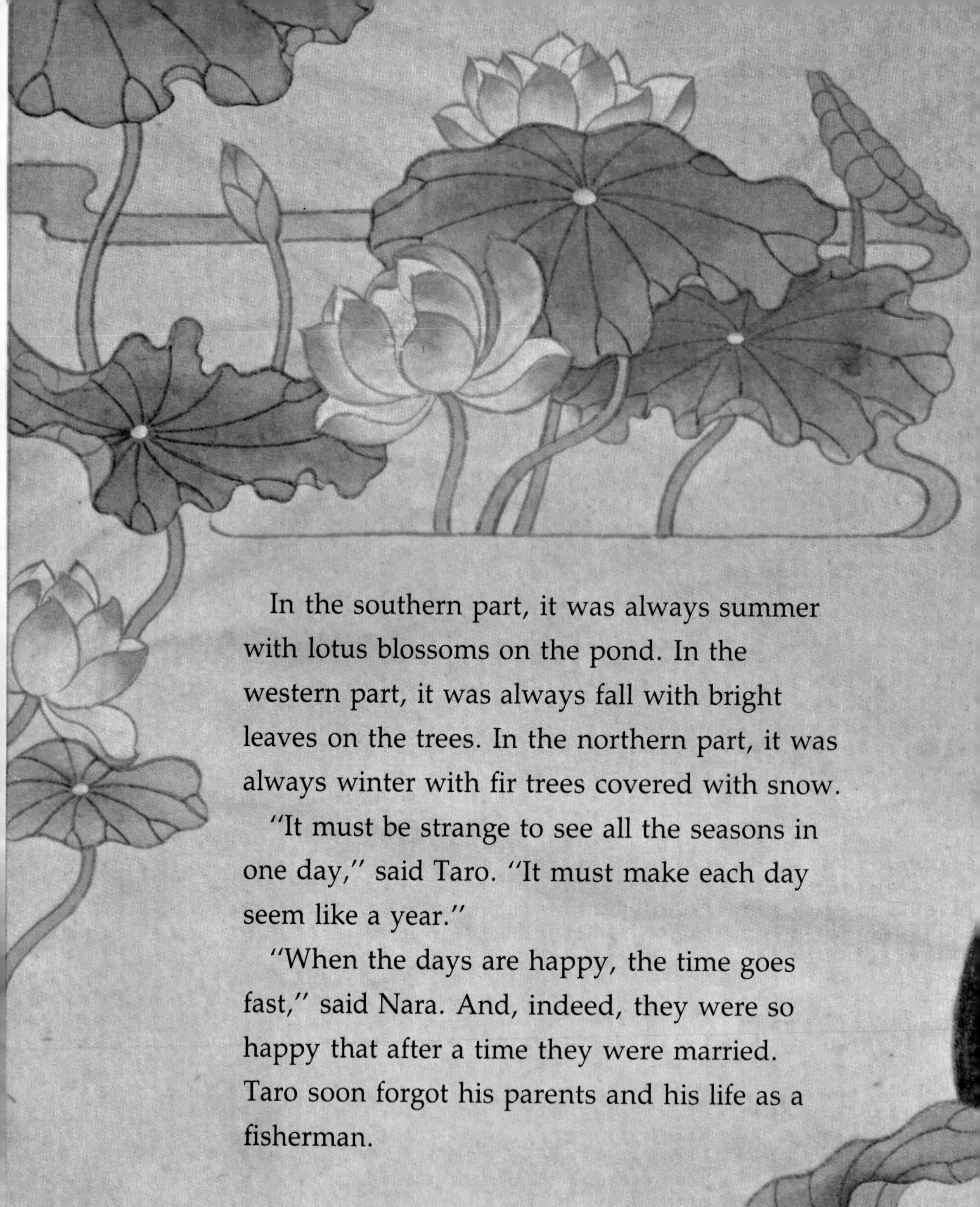

In the southern part, it was always summer with lotus blossoms on the pond. In the western part, it was always fall with bright leaves on the trees. In the northern part, it was always winter with fir trees covered with snow.

"It must be strange to see all the seasons in one day," said Taro. "It must make each day seem like a year."

"When the days are happy, the time goes fast," said Nara. And, indeed, they were so happy that after a time they were married. Taro soon forgot his parents and his life as a fisherman.

Then one day, Nara saw that Taro looked unhappy. "What is wrong?" she asked.

"It is my parents," said Taro. "They must wonder where I am. I must go home."

"Please do not leave me," said Nara in an unhappy voice.

"It will be for just a day," said Taro.

"Very well," said Nara. "Here is a gift so that you won't forget me." She gave Taro a gold box. "You must promise not to open this box. If you do, something terrible will happen."

"I promise," said Taro, hardly listening. He hurried to the beach, where another tortoise agreed to take him home.

Up, up swam the tortoise, with Taro holding tight. Then, all of a sudden, his head came up through the waves, and there was the sky! And the rocks along the sea coast! And the mountains covered with fir trees! And his village! Never had he seen anything so lovely.

"Soon I will see my parents," said Taro. He ran up the path to his hut. How happy they would be to see him!

But what had happened? The hut was now a large house. The woman who came to the door was a stranger.

"What are you doing here?" asked Taro. "Who are you?"

"This is my house!" said the woman. "I live here."

"How can that be?" asked Taro. "I have lived here with my parents all my life. I have not been gone long."

"Who are you?" asked the woman.

"Urashima Taro, of course. Everybody in this village knows me."

"You must be joking," said the woman. "Everybody knows that Urashima Taro was lost in his fishing boat three hundred years ago. It is a well-known story. Do not joke with me. Now, off with you."

Taro walked slowly down the path to the beach. Nobody knew him. All the houses looked different. It must be true. Three hundred years had gone by. Three years in the Land Under-the-Sea must have been the same as three hundred years here. How sad and lonely he felt.

"There must be a way to go back now," he thought. "Maybe something in this box will help me go back to the amazing Land Under-the-Sea."

He opened the box, forgetting his promise. A puff of white smoke came out. Suddenly he was an unsteady old man and, in a short time, was no longer among the living.

To this day, a very old tortoise visits the beach near Urashima Taro's village. It seems to be looking for something—or someone.

THINK ABOUT IT

1. How did Taro save the tortoise's life?
2. Who was the tortoise?
3. Why did Taro want to leave the Land Under-the-Sea for just one day?
4. Why didn't Taro remember Nara's words about the box?
5. Who was the old tortoise who visited the beach?
6. If you were taken to a magic land, what would you want that land to be like?
7. If you were suddenly to become old, what do you think you would look like?

Pencil Puppets

To make a pencil puppet, you will need two sheets of heavy paper, crayons, scissors, paint, glue, and pencils. You might also want to decorate the puppet with pieces of colored paper, yarn, and buttons.

Created by Dr. John Lidstone, Queens College of the City University of New York, Consultant in Art Education.

You can make pencil puppets that look like many different people. What do people in different jobs or careers look like? You can spot police officers and fire fighters by their clothes. But truck drivers or window washers don't wear special clothes. You cannot always tell what people do by the clothes they wear. Use your own ideas to design a puppet of a career person.

1 Draw or trace your puppet with a pencil on a sheet of heavy paper.

2 Carefully following the lines, cut out the shape of your puppet.

3 Trace around the cutout shape on another piece of heavy paper. Cut out this shape, too.

4 Use one shape as the front of the puppet and the other as the back. Color or paint each side.

5 To decorate your puppet, glue on colored paper, yarn, or buttons.

6 Glue together all the edges of your puppet but leave the bottom edge open.

7 Slip a pencil through the bottom edges of your puppet. Now you are ready to put on a puppet show.

Maybe your friends will help you put on a puppet show. You may want to make more pencil puppets that show people with different careers—a doctor, a farmer, or a clown.

Fire Fighters

On the thirtieth of May—the day of the big fire—Jerry Wise decided to be a fire fighter.

Jerry was asleep when the fire started. He was awakened by the sounds of fire trucks and the more than fifty fire fighters in the street below. He saw red-and-yellow flames shooting out of the windows of the building across the street. He saw thick black smoke pouring into the night sky.

He also saw the fire fighters rushing in and out of the burning building for what seemed like the fiftieth time.

At school the next day, everyone was buzzing about the fire. The children asked question after question about fire fighters.

"How do you get to be a fire fighter?" asked Jerry.

"Do fire fighters sleep in their boots?" asked Tony.

"Who has the toughest job of all the fire fighters?" asked June.

175
20

Without waiting for Mr. King, the teacher, to answer, Betty asked the fourth question.

"What does the fire chief do?" she said.

Then Jerry took another turn. "What makes the water come out of the fire hoses so fast?" he asked. "What are those nets made of? What . . . ?"

"Wait a minute, class," laughed Mr. King. "One question at a time. That's the sixth one already!"

Mr. King looked around at the class. "I will make plans to have all your questions answered tomorrow by an expert in fire fighting," he said with a smile.

The next day, Jerry couldn't wait to get to school. He thought of at least twenty things he wanted to know about fire fighting.

"Class," said Mr. King, "I want you to meet Chief Crossby of Engine Company Number 36. His company fought the big fire the other night. He'll be able to tell you all you want to know about fire fighting."

"So you want to know all about fires and fire fighters, do you?" began Chief Crossby. "All right. Now let's suppose that it's late at night, down at the firehouse. A call for help has come in. Here's what would happen."

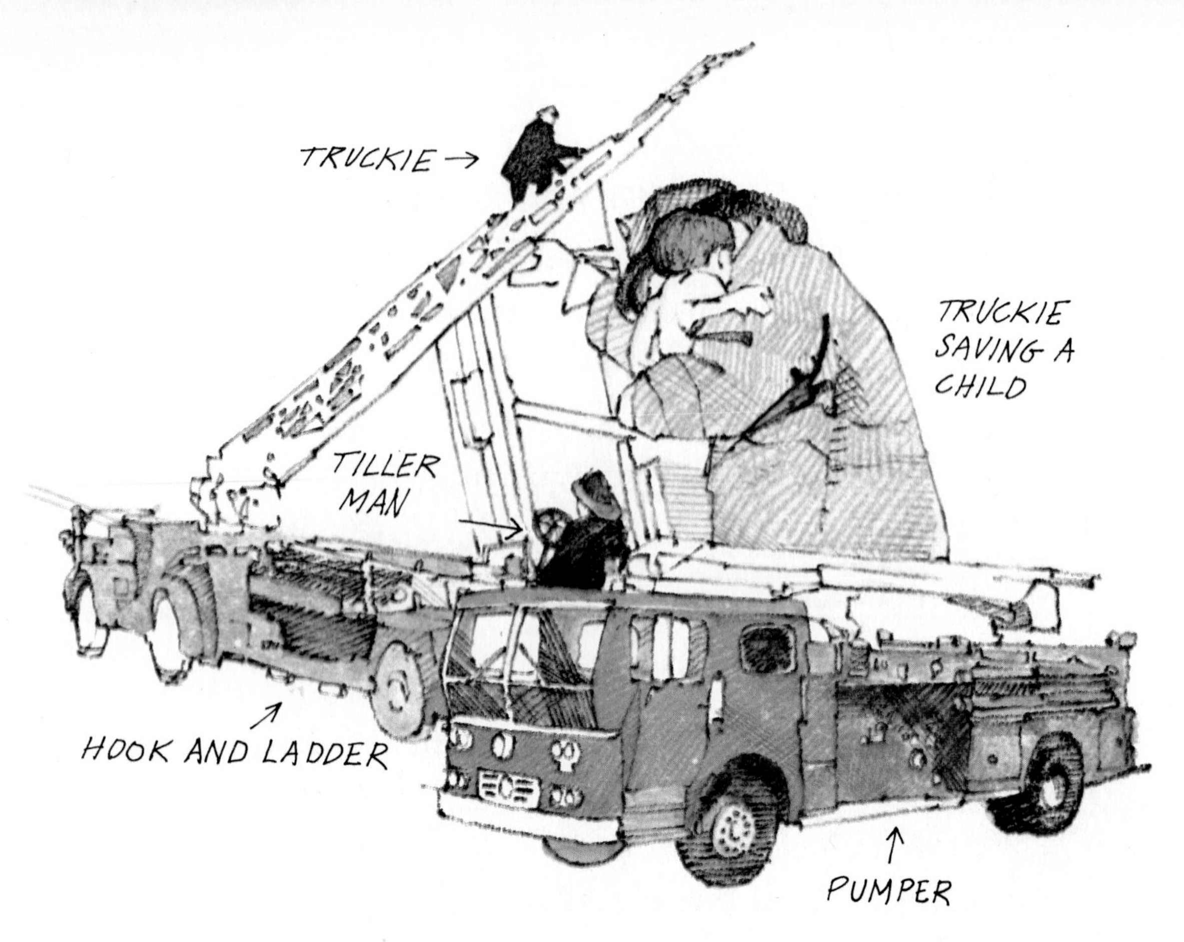

Chief Crossby seemed to look straight at Jerry. "When the call comes in, the fire fighters swing their feet through their pants and into their boots," the chief said. "They pull up their pants, grab their shirts—and are ready to go! This is called a 'thirty-second turnout.'

"Waterproof coats, helmets, and safety belts are waiting for them on the fire truck. Fire fighters can't waste a second, because every wasted second gives the fire a chance to spread."

Chief Crossby took a deep breath before going on. "I recall one fire on the twentieth of last month," he said. "That one was what we call a 'worker.' That means it was a really hard building fire to put out.

"We used every truck in the department for that one—the hook-and-ladder and the pumpers. The pumper truck forces the water through the fire hydrants and into the hoses.

"You see, every truck has its own special job and its own special team of trained fire fighters. The people who ride the hook-and-ladder trucks are called 'truckies.' Their first and most important job is to save anyone who may not be able to get out of a burning building.

"The truckie climbs up the ten-story ladder attached to the truck. Then, very slowly and very carefully, the fire fighter backs down the ladder, carrying the person being rescued.

"The person who sits high on the back of the hook-and-ladder truck is called the 'tiller man.' His main job is to steer the back of the long truck around street corners."

"I'm going to be a tiller man," Jerry thought when he heard that. "I'm going to steer the back of the hook-and-ladder truck."

Chief Crossby went on. "Sometimes, the ladder can't reach high enough to rescue someone trapped above the tenth floor of a building," he said. "So then the fire fighter uses a rifle which shoots a rope high into the air. The rope attaches itself to a ledge or some other part of the building.

"Sometimes, I have to order the fire fighters to 'open up' the fire. They do this by cutting holes in the roof with their axes to let the smoke and heat out.

"The people who ride the pumper trucks are called 'smoke eaters.' They jump off the pumper truck as soon as it stops. Then they attach a short fat hose to the fire hydrant. This hose carries the water from the hydrant to the pumper. They pull the long, heavy hoses off the truck—these are the fire hoses—and begin fighting the fire.

"The smoke eaters work hard," the chief went on. "They have to in order to keep the hoses from jumping out of their hands. Tons of water pour through the hoses, and the force of the water is very strong."

"That's it!" Jerry thought to himself. "That's what I'm going to be, a smoke eater!"

Betty waved her hand. "What does the chief do?" she asked.

"My job is to make sure that the fire is brought under control," said the chief. "I have to know when to replace equipment or fire fighters. And I have to make sure that the Thirty-Sixth is in the right place at the right time!"

Chief Crossby looked around at the class. "Of course, there's more to being a fire fighter than riding on fire engines or fighting fires," he said. "You've got to keep every piece of equipment in perfect working order. The fire fighters spend hours checking and repairing equipment. They even return to school to learn new ways to fight fires. Some of them learn how to work on fireboats or jump from airplanes to fight forest fires.

"Maybe the most important lesson they learn is this: Each person's safety depends upon the other people in the company. The fire fighters all must work as part of a team. The safety of this school depends upon the Thirty-Sixth. Any questions?"

Jerry's hand shot up into the air. "When can I sign up?" he asked.

Chief Crossby smiled. “Well,” he said, “we can always use good people. But I don’t think we have a thirty-second turnout suit to fit you, at least not yet. How about in ten years?”

“I’ll be there,” said Jerry. “You can depend on me!”

“And on me!” said Betty.

THINK ABOUT IT

1. When a call comes in, how long do the fire fighters have to get ready?
2. Which fire truck is used to force the water from a fire hydrant into the hose?
3. What different kinds of jobs do fire fighters have?
4. Why was it a good idea for Chief Crossby to come to talk to the class?
5. Why did Jerry think that he would like to be a tiller man and a smoke eater?
6. Can you think of other jobs in which a person’s safety depends upon others?

A Citizen of Two Countries

Carlos wished his English was better. He wished he did not miss his island home, his friends, his baseball team. He wished he and his family had not come to the United States.

Carlos remembered what his friend, the Governor of Puerto Rico, had told him. "You are already a citizen of the United States."

Carlos tried to feel good about that, but it was hard—especially when he went to the playground. Today, as he watched the boys and girls playing baseball, Carlos felt even lonelier and more confused than before.

Suddenly he saw the ball coming his way. He jumped high and caught it. "Good catch!" said a boy called Sam. Carlos smiled.

Then John, the pitcher, spoke. "Give me that ball!" he said roughly.

REDS

Carlos felt the sting in John's voice. John had been making fun of him ever since he said he was a citizen of two countries.

"Oh, stop it, John," Sam snapped. "Maybe Carlos *is* a citizen of two countries."

"If he is a citizen of another country, then he is a foreigner," said John.

"Foreigner—what is that?" Carlos asked.

"It means you're not an American citizen," John snapped.

"I am so!" Carlos said.

"Aren't you Puerto Rican?" said John, confused.

"Yes," Carlos spoke proudly. "But I am an American, too. I am *both!* You can even ask my friend, the Governor of Puerto Rico."

"How come you know the Governor?" asked John.

Carlos said. "I used to take milk to his house. Sometimes we talked. Señor Luis Muñoz Marín became my friend."

"Well, that may be so," said John. "But I still say a citizen of another country is a foreigner." He grabbed the ball roughly from Carlos and walked away.

That evening at home, Carlos thought unhappily about this day. How could he explain about being a citizen of two countries? If he wrote to the Governor for help, would the Governor answer? "The Governor could explain why I'm a Puerto Rican *and* an American," thought Carlos.

So Carlos wrote a letter, wishing he could fly back to Puerto Rico with it.

Soon the answer came. Carlos tore open the letter. He was afraid to see what it contained. But after reading the letter, Carlos could not wait to tell the girls and boys, especially John. He hurried to the playground.

"I have something to show you, John! It is a letter from my friend, the Governor of Puerto Rico!" Carlos handed John the letter.

The other children crowded around to read the news that the letter contained.

"I'll read it," Sam said, and John handed him the letter. Then Sam read aloud.

Office of the Governor

Dear Carlos:

I miss seeing you these days. We haven't found a boy to replace you. I know it is a new experience for you in the United States, and you are upset and confused. You will get along all right, if you continue to try to make friends in your new home.

Now to answer your question. Yes, Carlos, you are a citizen of two countries--of Puerto Rico, and of the United States. Puerto Ricans were made United States citizens in 1926, by law. Puerto Rico was made a free Commonwealth in 1952.

You really should be proud. Not many people can boast about being a citizen of two countries!

I hope this letter contains the information you need. I wish you well.

Your friend,

Luis Muñoz Marín, Governor
Commonwealth of Puerto Rico

Sam smiled at Carlos. "This letter sure is something," he said. "You can write back and tell him we're happy to have you here with us." Then, turning to John, he added, "We need a good fielder like Carlos on our team. Right, John?"

John looked at Sam and then at Carlos. "Let's not just stand around. We have a game to play," he said, smiling. "You can play left field, Carlos."

Carlos looked at the other girls and boys. "I am proud to be on your team," he said. "Very proud."

THINK ABOUT IT

1. Why did Carlos wish that his family had not moved to the United States?
2. Why did Carlos decide to write to the Governor of Puerto Rico?
3. What was the first thing the Governor said to Carlos in his letter?
4. How did John use the word *foreigner* when he spoke to Carlos?
5. How do you think John would feel in Puerto Rico?
6. What would be the hardest thing for you if you were suddenly to move to a new place?

WATERMELON SEEDS

"What did you bury there?" a deep voice said.

Jody looked up fearfully at the man in work clothes. "Just some watermelon seeds," she said.

"Dig, please," the school custodian said.

Quickly Jody dug up the small plot. She held out some large seeds. "Just some watermelon seeds," she repeated. "This is the only place around here to plant anything."

"Watermelons can't grow here!" the custodian said. "Besides, I don't want anyone disturbing this place. So let's not discuss it anymore."

"I won't disturb anything," Jody said.

The custodian thought about Jody and the seeds. At last he said, "Well, I guess there's no harm in trying to plant seeds while school is closed for the summer. But watermelons! Look, I don't have any more time to discuss it, but believe me, melons will not grow here."

Jody thought as he left her, "I'll make them grow! Surely the warm earth will help the seeds to sprout. Maybe in a week I'll see a leaf."

But when a week went by, Jody began to think that the custodian might be right. She had carried bucket after bucket of water to the little plot. No matter how much she looked after the plot, it never seemed to have enough water. Jody was getting disgusted with the whole idea, but she continued to hope.

When the custodian returned, he was surprised to see Jody in the same spot.

"Are you still at it?" he asked.

"They'll grow," Jody insisted.

The custodian shook his head and walked away. Suddenly two older boys arrived.

"What have you buried there?" one boy asked.

"Maybe she's a thief hiding stolen jewels," the other boy said. Picking up a stick, he used it like a knife to dig into the ground.

"Stop!" cried Jody. "*You* are the thief! You're both thieves! *I* never stole anything!"

Using sticks like knives, the boys continued to dig. "There's nothing here but seeds!" they cried.

"That's my garden!" Jody said angrily. "You thieves! You've dug up my seeds!"

"I don't get it!" the leader said disgustedly. The boys left just as quickly as they had come.

Jody was worried because her seeds had been disturbed. How could they sprout now? Then she saw it—a seed with a tiny threadlike root! She knelt down and gently picked up some seeds. These seeds seemed to be sprouting, too! Carefully Jody replanted and watered them. The dry earth seemed to drink up the water.

The next time Jody spotted the custodian, she rushed to meet him. "Look there!" she said, pointing proudly at four plants with tiny leaves.

"How interesting!" The custodian grinned as he studied the small plants. "Maybe we should discuss this," he said. "Why do you think watermelon vines will make this school better?"

For a few minutes, Jody did not answer. She looked at the dull gray buildings and at the paper thrown in the street. Then she explained. "It won't make the school better," she said. "But green vines are pretty. Once I saw a school building all covered with vines, and I wished I could go to school there. How long do you think it would take to grow flowers and long vines?" she asked excitedly.

"What is your name," asked the custodian.

"Jody Soong," she answered.

"Well, Jody, will you meet me here at this time tomorrow?" asked the custodian. "I'll have your answer then."

"Yes, I'll meet you here." But she wondered *why?* Would he make her pull up the sprouts? She could not bear that. This time she would surely give up in disgust.

The next day, the custodian arrived with some plants. "These," he said, "are ivy plants already rooted. Ivy can grow in poor earth next to buildings. I suspect it was ivy you saw once on a school building. Is this the school you'll be going to in the fall?"

Jody's eyes were wide as she nodded.

"Well, plant these against the wall here," said the custodian. "When school opens there should be some vines growing on the wall."

"Thank you, thank you for helping me!" Jody cried.

"It looks as if we've helped each other and the school as well," he said.

They smiled happily at each other.

THINK ABOUT IT

1. What did Jody want to grow?
2. What did the older children think Jody was hiding?
3. How did the custodian help Jody?
4. How did Jody feel when she saw a tiny root?
5. Did the older children feel bad about digging up Jody's garden?
6. Why do you think the custodian did not help Jody in the beginning?
7. What have you ever done that has taken time and work? How did you feel when you were finished?

RUDOLPH IS TIRED OF THE CITY

These buildings are too close to me.
I'd like to PUSH away.
I'd like to live in the country,
And spread my arms all day.

I'd like to spread my breath out, too—
As farmers' sons and daughters do.

I'd tend the cows and chickens.
I'd do the other chores.
Then, all the hours left I'd go
A-SPREADING out-of-doors.

Gwendolyn Brooks

A Way to Remember

"Tina," said Dad. "Come straight home from school today. We're going to Grandma's birthday party."

Tina smiled. "Oh, Dad," she said. "You never forget anything!"

"That's because I have a special helper," said Dad. "Come here, and I'll show it to you."

JUNE

SUN.	MON.	TUES.	WED.	THURS.	FRI.	SAT.
		1	2	3	4	5
6	7	8	9	10 Grandma's Birthday	11	12
13	14 Flag Day	15 Tina: School Field Day	16	17	18	19
20 Father's Day	21 Tina: Doctor 3:30	22	23	24	25 Last Day of School	26
27	28	29	30			

Do you know what Dad's helper is called? It is a calendar. This calendar is in the form of a chart. It tells you certain things in a way that helps you to understand them quickly and clearly. Many calendars have a space for writing things you want to remember.

Look at the page from Dad's calendar. What month is it? Where is the month shown?

On the calendar, find the names of the days of the week. Say the name of each day. Which name is shown first? Which name is shown last?

The rest of the calendar is broken up into squares. The numeral in each square tells you the day of the month. On what day of the week did the first day of June fall?

Answer these questions about Dad's calendar.

1. On which day of the *month* is Grandma's birthday?
2. On which day of the *week* is Grandma's birthday?
3. Where is Tina going on June 15? On which day of the week does June 15 fall?
4. On which day is Tina going to the doctor?
5. When is the last day of school?

Make a calendar of your own for the present month and year. In the squares write what you have already done this month. Then write what you plan to do later in the month.

five

The Floating Stone

CHARACTERS

First Court Lady
Second Court Lady
Third Court Lady
The Princess
The Shepherd
The King
The Prince of Arna
The Prince of Tripota

SCENE I

SETTING: *A King's court.*

First Lady: I must say that I like my stay at your court, but there is one thing I can't understand. I think it is my duty to tell you.

Second Lady: What is that?

First Lady: Your Princess is so beautiful, so dutiful, and so honest—why doesn't she marry and have a court of her own?

Second Lady (*Whispering*): Sh-h-h.

First Lady (*Whispering*): What's the matter?

Second Lady: Don't say *marry.* The King won't hear of it. He is so mean to visiting princes that they go home.

First Lady: Poor Princess!

Second Lady: I don't believe she minds.

First Lady: I don't understand.

Second Lady: You see, she is in love with a young shepherd. He never can hope to marry her, but at least she doesn't have to marry someone else. (*Third Lady enters.*)

Third Lady: Have you heard the news?

Second Lady: What news?

Third Lady: You haven't heard yet? Why, everyone in court is laughing about it!

First and Second Ladies: Tell us!

Third Lady: The King, the King—(*She laughs.*) He says the Princess can marry if she likes!

First Lady: When?

Second Lady: Who?

Third Lady: The man who can make a stone float in the air!

First Lady: Make a stone *float* in the air!

Third Lady: That's his fanciful way of keeping the Princess by his side always.

First Lady: Poor Princess. (*They all go out.*)

SCENE II

Princess: Now there is some hope for us.

Shepherd: Is there? I would do anything in the world to marry you, but how can I make a stone float in the air?

Princess: Here is a paper my father gave me. He said it would help.

Shepherd: Let me see. (*He opens the paper.*) It says, "Try science." What's science? Wait, there's more!
"They who by science would be led
Must learn to look inside their heads."

Princess: "They who by science would be led . . ." What does that mean?

Shepherd: I don't know, but at least I can try to find out so that we may marry. (*They leave.*)

SCENE III

King: Daughter, this is the day when young men may ask for your hand. It is their duty to make a stone—a very small stone—float in the air. I am sure that the man who really loves you will have no trouble at all.

Princess (*Softly*)**:** If only my Shepherd comes in time.

King: Ah, here is your first suitor.

Prince of Arna: I am the Prince of Arna. I have learned from the stars that your beautiful daughter and I will marry.

King: Indeed! Well, there is the stone on that silver cloth on the table.

Prince of Arna (*Going to the table*): Dark stars and bright stars—(*He can't remember the words.*) Something, something, and bright stars. I'm not sure I remember all the fanciful words in the magic spell. Some of them are quite long.

Princess: Maybe you really don't want to try.

Prince of Arna: I think the stone did rise a little.

Princess: I am sure it didn't. I was watching.

King: Away with you, Prince of Arna. It is my duty to tell you that my daughter shall not marry such a fool. (*The Prince of Arna leaves. The Prince of Tripota enters.*) Ah, my dear Princess, your second suitor has arrived.

Prince of Tripota: I have come to move mountains to marry the Princess.

King: Oh, no, not mountains—just a very small stone. I don't even ask that it float in the air for long—half a minute will do.

Prince of Tripota: Most beautiful lady, show me the stone, and I shall make it float.

Princess: It is on the table.

Prince of Tripota: Abracadabra! Abracadabra! (*He drops a cloth over the stone.*) When I take this cloth away, the stone will float into the air. (*He pulls the cloth away; his face falls.*)

King: Well, Prince of Tripota, it seems as if you are not moving any mountains this day. (*The Prince of Tripota leaves; the Shepherd enters.*) Ah, dear Princess, your third suitor has arrived.

Shepherd: And I shall marry your daughter!

King: Don't be too sure, Shepherd. Two princes have already tried—and lost.

Shepherd: Let me try, Your Majesty. You said that anyone who made the stone float could ask the Princess to marry him.

King: There lies the stone. But tell me, where did a shepherd learn magic?

Shepherd: This is not magic. This is science.

Shepherd (*Smiling at the King*):

"They who by science would be led
Must learn to look inside their heads."

King (*Smiling back at the Shepherd*)**:** And did you look inside your head?

Shepherd: Yes, Your Majesty. Look! (*He takes some tools from his bag and grinds the stone.*)

Princess: He's grinding the stone into powder!

Shepherd: Look, Your Majesty, the stone is ready to float. (*He puts the powder into his hand. Then he holds both hands in front of his lips and blows the powder into the air.*)

King: You may marry my daughter, if she will have you, Shepherd. I wanted to be sure she married a man who could use his head.

THINK ABOUT IT

1. What did the King decide a man must do in order to marry his daughter?
2. Whom did the Princess really love?
3. Why did the Second Lady say that a shepherd could never marry a princess?
4. Did the King like what the Shepherd said to him?
5. Why did the King want the Princess's husband to be able to use his head?
6. Do you think that the King's test was a fair one? Why or why not?

Papa's Birthday

"Let's all save our pennies faithfully for the next week," said Ella. "Then we'll have enough money to buy Papa a birthday present."

"I'll save my pennies," said little Gertie. Sarah and Charlotte and Henny agreed.

Every day, as always, Mama gave each of the girls a penny to spend as she pleased. Each day for a week, the others faithfully turned over their pennies to Ella, the oldest sister.

The last day of the week the children made their way to Mr. Pincus's bargain store. This part of the city was crowded with people and run-down houses. The girls loved to walk through the busy streets and hear the noise of machines making all kinds of things. Sometimes they would even visit the shop that was Papa's business.

All around them they heard the Yiddish language spoken, for many Jewish people lived here. This was where Mama came often to buy the food for the Jewish dishes she cooked.

Ella and Sarah and Henny and Charlotte and Gertie came at last to Mr. Pincus's bargain store. Mr. Pincus tried hard to be helpful. He pulled things off high shelves for them. He unpacked boxes. How about a tie? How about a nice fancy comb and brush set?

But nothing he showed them was right.

The girls were becoming unhappy. Suddenly Gertie noticed something. "Look at that pretty cup and saucer," she cried.

It was the most wonderful cup and saucer they had ever seen. It was made of glowing blue-and-white china. On the front, in gold lettering, was the word *Father.* There was even a ledge across one side of the cup. It would keep Papa's moustache from getting wet when he drank his coffee.

"She's a good picker, that little one," Mr. Pincus beamed as he wrapped the present.

That night they waited eagerly for Papa's homecoming. The present in its wrapping lay at his place at the table. The beaming girls hopped about excitedly. They said over and over, "I wish Papa would come home! Oh, how I wish Papa would come home!"

Papa came at last. His footsteps on the stairs were slow and heavy tonight. It had been a long, hard day at the shop, with very little money coming in. Papa looked very weary.

The children were so eager to surprise their father that they didn't notice how weary he was. They crowded about him. "Happy birthday, Papa!" They could hardly wait.

He smiled a weary little smile. "Thank you all for remembering," he said.

There was a rush to the table. Everyone wanted to be there when he found the gift.

"What's this?" Papa asked as he sat down.

"A present from your daughters," Mama said, beaming.

"A present for *me*?" He'd never had a present from the children before. He turned the gift round and round in his hands.

"Aren't you going to unwrap it?" Henny said.

"Yes, of course." Papa untied the string. The paper fell away. The china cup and saucer with the special ledge for Papa's moustache stood on the table. Papa stared at his present and said not a word about it.

The girls were confused. What was wrong? What made Papa's face look so sorrowful? Didn't he like their gift? Wasn't the moustache ledge a wonderful idea? Should they have bought something else?

However, Papa was thinking: "So much money spent on some fancy china that I could just as well do without."

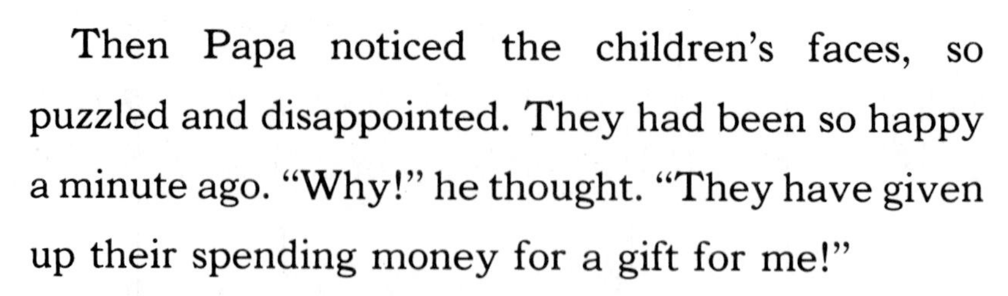

Then Papa noticed the children's faces, so puzzled and disappointed. They had been so happy a minute ago. "Why!" he thought. "They have given up their spending money for a gift for me!"

"You look disappointed," Ella said. "We should have bought something more useful."

Papa smiled his wide gentle smile at his daughters. "No, no, it's wonderful! How did you ever come to think of it? I'm so happy. I can't wait to use my new coffee cup."

Again the room seemed to be filled with sunshine and joy. Papa found himself with five laughing daughters. They eagerly ran to him for a hug and a big kiss.

THINK ABOUT IT

1. What did the girls save their money for?
2. How did Mama feel about the gift?
3. What was Papa's first thought when he saw his gift?
4. What kind of family did this family seem to be?
5. Why did Papa feel the way he did about his gift?
6. What do you think makes a gift special?
7. What is the most special gift that you have ever given someone? What is the most special gift that you have ever received? Why were they special?

SECOND CHANCE FOR KING

Tim Oliver sat on his front steps with tears in his eyes. He had just been told by his father that he was about to lose his best friend.

Tim's best friend was a dog named King. King had arrived in Mr. Oliver's arms on Tim's sixth birthday. Tim and King had been best friends ever since.

"How often have I told you not to bury things that don't belong to you?" Tim asked King. "For the hundredth time, I'm telling you that only thieves take things that don't belong to them."

King wagged his tail and looked up at Tim's unhappy face.

"If you understood what's going to happen," said Tim, "you wouldn't wag your tail."

King wagged his tail again and tugged at Tim's arm.

"No, King," said Tim angrily. "We can't play now. I have to talk to you. Sit down and listen to me."

King sat down, still wagging his tail.

"Dad says I have to send you away," said Tim. "He is angry because you keep taking things. He doesn't understand that you're just interested in things."

King just looked up at Tim.

"I told Dad you never take anything of value," said Tim. He brushed away the new tears that had started to run down his face. "I told him the only thing of value you ever took from anybody was that old leather pouch you found on our porch. I even told him that we returned the pouch the very next day to the girl who delivers the papers."

Tim sighed. "But Dad just shook his head. He says it's all the same—a leather pouch or an old shoe. He says if you take what doesn't belong to you, it's stealing."

"Your father's right, Tim," said Mrs. Oliver, coming out of the house quickly. "But I've been listening, and I've been thinking. Maybe we can do something to help King learn not to take other people's things. Maybe we can send King to school."

"School!" cried Tim, opening his eyes wide. "What kind of school teaches dogs?"

"A dog-training school," said Mrs. Oliver. She sat on the steps next to Tim. "Many people send their dogs there to learn how to obey," she said.

"How are they trained?" asked Tim, getting more and more interested.

"It's very interesting," said Mrs. Oliver. "The dog is given an order. Each time it obeys, it is rewarded. The reward may be a pat on the head, or it may be something the dog likes to eat."

"What happens if the dog doesn't obey?" asked Tim, looking at King.

"The trainer will repeat the order," said Mrs. Oliver. "It is repeated and repeated until the dog obeys. Then the dog gets a reward. In this way, the dog is taught to obey because it wants to please its trainer and get a reward."

"That's how I taught King to retrieve a stick," said Tim with a laugh.

"That's right, Tim," said Mrs. Oliver. "You taught King to retrieve a stick. Maybe you can teach him not to take our belongings."

"Do you think Dad will let King go to school?" asked Tim.

"Why don't you and King ask him?" said Mrs. Oliver.

"That's a great idea!" Tim said.

As Tim told him about the idea for King, Mr. Oliver sat quietly.

"What do you think, Dad?" asked Tim. "They may be able to teach King not to steal our things. Please, can't we try it? I'm sure King could learn quickly. Mom thinks it's a good idea."

Mr. Oliver looked at his son's pleading face. Then he looked down at King. King seemed to be pleading, too.

"Very well, Tim," said Mr. Oliver. "We'll give King another chance. But this means you'll have to give up your summer vacation at Aunt Betty's house on Summer Island. You can't go to Summer Island and to dog-training school, too. You must be willing to go to school with King. That way he will learn to obey your orders. And you will learn how to give orders."

"Keeping King is better than any vacation trip to Summer Island," shouted Tim, throwing his arms around King.

"Hold on now," said Mr. Oliver. "I haven't said you could keep King yet. I just said we'd give him another chance. We'll have to wait and see how well King learns his lessons."

"He'll learn," said Tim happily. "I'll help him!"

So the next week, when vacation from school began, Tim and King arrived early at dog-training school.

Every day they went to school, and every day they worked hard. Often, they had to repeat a lesson. But Tim and King didn't mind.

Each night when they returned from school, Tim gave his parents a report on what they had learned that day. Each time Tim finished his report, Mr. Oliver smiled and nodded. However, he never discussed keeping King.

Week after week went by. Soon everyone in the family saw that King was not stealing anymore. Shoes and socks were no longer missing. Even Mr. Oliver began to like having King around.

Then one day, the lessons at the dog-training school were over.

"You and King have done a fine job, Tim," said Mrs. Rice, the woman who ran the school. "I never saw a boy or a dog work so hard."

Tim thanked Mrs. Rice and left the school. Outside on the street, he stopped to pet King. Then together they hurried home to give Mr. and Mrs. Oliver the good report.

That night, just before Tim went to sleep, he stopped to say good night to King. "You can stay, King," he said happily. "Dad and Mom are proud of both of us. You're a smart dog and a lucky one, too. It isn't every dog that gets a second chance."

King wagged his tail!

THINK ABOUT IT

1. Why did Mr. Oliver decide that King had to leave?
2. What idea did Mrs. Oliver have?
3. Why did Mr. Oliver make Tim go to school with King?
4. Why didn't Mr. Oliver promise Tim that he would be able to keep King after he finished dog-training school?
5. Why do you think it might be hard to train a dog?
6. What kind of person makes a good dog owner?

Have you ever seen actors use their faces and hands to help make their words come alive? When you use ink or paint or crayons or scissors, you can make your own words come alive. Read the next page carefully, and then try to make some words of your own come alive.

1 Make "drip" or "spill" come alive by using ink or paint on wet paper.

Created by Dr. John Lidstone, Queens College of the City University of New York, Consultant in Art Education.

2.
Spell out "shrink" or "stretch" with torn paper glued to construction paper.
SHRINK
3
Cut paper in a design that you think looks like a "slant" or a "cloud."
SLANT
CLOUD
4
Use thick gobs of paint, crayon, or glue to make "sticky" or "bumpy" come alive.
STICKY

BEACH FIRE

When the picnic was over,
We sat by the tide
And watched the white-winged
Sea gulls slide

Down the evening wind.
The stars came out
Above the sea,
And Dad gave a shout:

"Oh, wish on that little
Brand-new moon!
Let's build up the fire
With wood from the dune!"

We wished on the moon,
We built up the fire,
We sang, while the sparks
Flew higher, higher

Like stars of our own
Above the foam,
Till, sleepy, we
And the birds went home.

Frances Frost

Voyage to Outer Space

"All aboard for outer space!" Dad said. "This afternoon you're going to the Planetarium, and you'll take a pretend rocket trip to the moon!"

"Wow, that sounds great!" John said. He and Jean had been talking about space and planets.

"What's the name of the place we're going to?" Jean asked.

"The Planetarium," said Dad. "A planetarium is a place where you can see planets and millions of stars on a big dome-shaped ceiling."

As they walked into the Planetarium, John took a deep breath. A strange green-blue light filled the auditorium. The air was cool after the outdoor heat of the summer afternoon. Music was playing.

Around the bottom edge of the dome-shaped ceiling stood the dark outline of the city's skyline—roofs of the lower buildings, the trees in the parks, the skyscrapers. In a few minutes, the auditorium was packed with people. The lights were shut off.

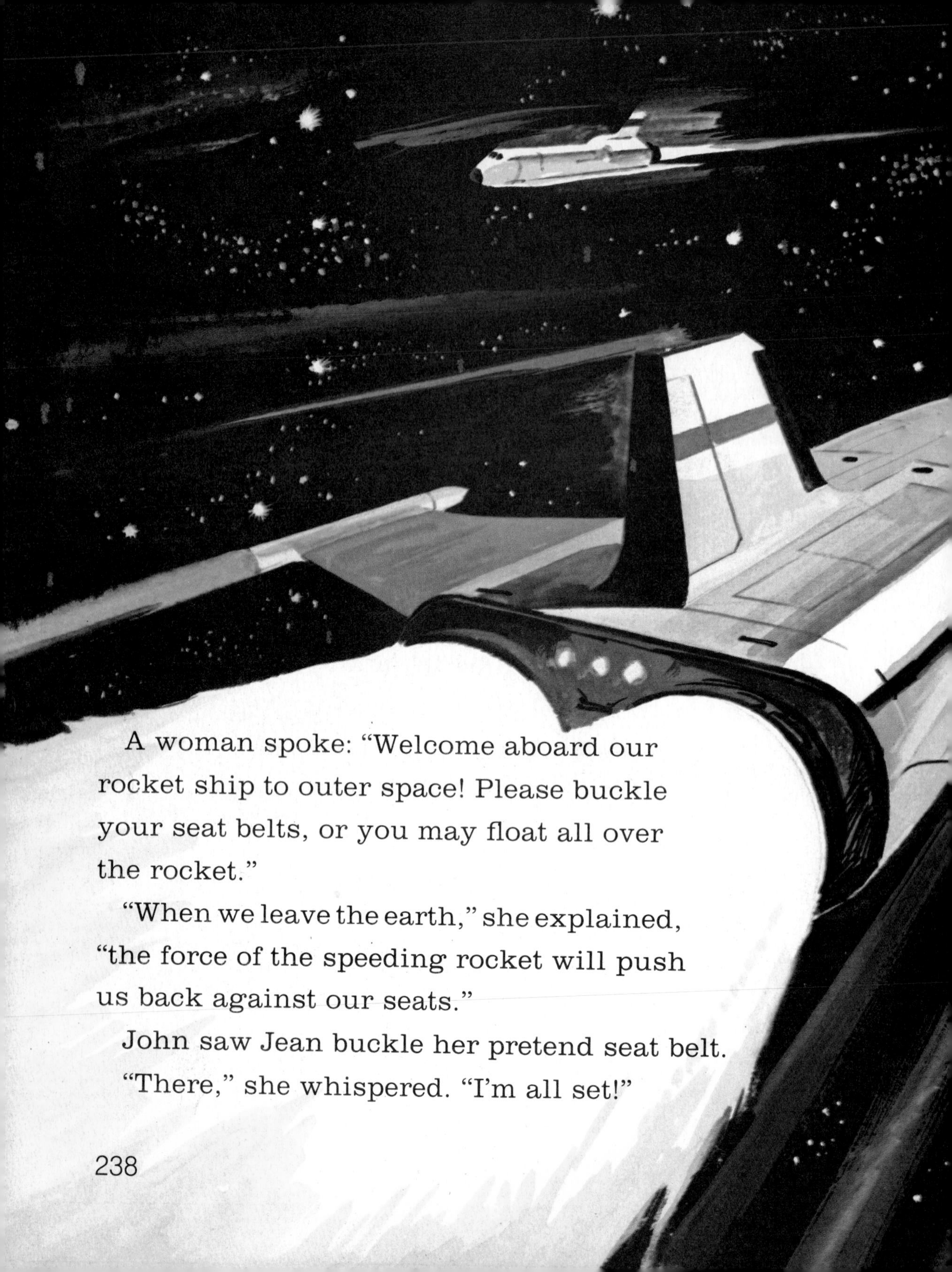

A woman spoke: "Welcome aboard our rocket ship to outer space! Please buckle your seat belts, or you may float all over the rocket."

"When we leave the earth," she explained, "the force of the speeding rocket will push us back against our seats."

John saw Jean buckle her pretend seat belt. "There," she whispered. "I'm all set!"

Then the woman's voice said, "Prepare for blast-off! Prepare for blast-off!"

Jean held onto John's hand. They leaned hard against the backs of their seats as the rocket engines roared. They were off for their pretend trip to the moon!

There ahead of them, through the space port, was a very small moon. As they went toward it, the moon grew bigger and bigger. It seemed to John that they were going to crash right into the big mountains. There was a sudden flash of light! Then the rocket engines stopped.

They were in a crater on the moon! Peaks around the edge of the crater were lit by the yellow light of the sun.

The sky was black and filled with millions of stars even while the sun was shining.

"Let's talk about what it would be like to be walking on the moon," the woman said. "Let's pretend to explore the moon."

There was no blue sky. There was only the bright light from the sun. "The earth would look a lot bigger from here than the moon does from the earth," Jean said.

"About four times bigger because it *is* bigger," John said.

"And, on the moon you would be much lighter than on the earth," the woman added. "You would be able to jump very high."

"At home my record for the high jump is five feet. Wow! I could jump thirty feet on the moon," John cried. "I could set a new record!"

"I remember why, John," said Jean. "It's because there is much more gravity on the earth. On the moon, we could jump six times as high or far."

"Just for fun, pretend you are jumping on the moon," the woman said.

"This is fun!" cried Jean. They had a wonderful time pretending. They were both out of breath from laughing.

"On the moon, you could pick up a big rock as if it were very light," the woman added.

"I would be much stronger on the moon than on the earth," Jean said.

"No, you would be the same as on the earth," John explained. "It's just that gravity wouldn't be forcing the rock down the way it does on earth. The moon hasn't as much gravity as earth has, remember," John said.

Just then the lights went on and off. The woman said, "The rocket is ready to blast off. Buckle your seat belts."

They buckled their pretend seat belts. The rocket engines roared once again. The top space port opened. Through the port, John and Jean saw millions of shiny stars and planets. They saw the earth growing bigger and bigger.

"Prepare for landing! Prepare for landing!" the woman's voice said.

A bright light flashed. John opened his eyes to the skyline of the city. Around the edge of the dome-shaped ceiling, he saw the roofs of the lower buildings, the trees in the parks, the skyscrapers. He shook himself to make sure he was back on earth.

As they left the auditorium, Dad said, "Welcome home! Did you have a nice voyage?"

"This was better than our trips to the seashore and the mountains," Jean said.

John grinned. "Wow! I'll say," he added. "It was the very best vacation voyage we ever had!"

THINK ABOUT IT

1. Although John and Jean were really at the Planetarium, where did they pretend they were?
2. On their pretend rocket trip, where did John and Jean land first?
3. Is the earth bigger than the moon? How much bigger?
4. Why did the rocket trip seem so real?
5. Would you like to take a real trip into outer space? Why or why not?

HAVE SOME FUN

Look at the cartoon on this page. Did it make you laugh? Why or why not?

How many boxes does the cartoon have? These boxes are called "panels." A cartoon that has more than one panel is called a "comic strip." What comic strip do *you* like best?

In the cartoon, where are the children's words printed? The white spaces with the words in them are called "balloons." Most comic strips use balloons to show what someone is saying.

Cut a comic strip out of a newspaper. Paste pieces of heavy white paper over the balloons. Then write your own words in the balloons. Be sure that what you write tells a story of some kind.

Now look at the cartoon on this page. How many panels does it have? Where are the speaker's words shown? Who is speaking? Most cartoons with only one panel put the speaker's words at the bottom.

"SMILE, MR. WILSON!"

Look through some of the other books you use in school. Do any of them have cartoons? Read the cartoons. How are they like the cartoons in this book? How are they different?

six

The Big Game

"Let's go, Teddy. Knock the ball out of the yard," shouted Jane. But she knew that he wouldn't. Teddy couldn't even hit the ball.

As the ball flew past Teddy, he shut his eyes and swung the bat. He opened his eyes when he heard the ball land in the catcher's mitt.

As always, Billy stepped up to give Teddy some help. "Keep your eyes on the ball."

Teddy smiled at his friend. Billy made it all sound so easy. For Billy, it was easy. Teddy was sure that Billy could slug a tiny pea across the yard if he wanted to.

"Come on, Teddy," urged Billy. "You can do it! Hit that ball!"

By the third pitch, Teddy remembered to keep his eyes open. But it was too late. He was out.

Just then some older children walked by.

"Great hitting," one of them called.

"You're a real hitter," said another.

In a flash, the players from Teddy's class 302 were on their feet.

"You big shots aren't such hot players," called Paul. "We saw you lose to class 506 last week."

"You couldn't catch a turtle," shouted Rosa.

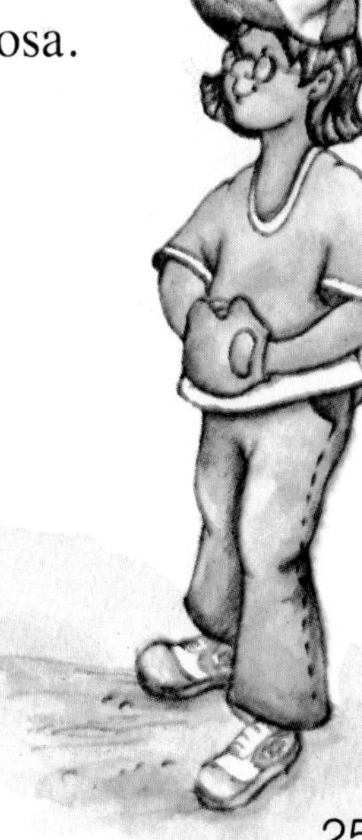

"We could beat you any day of the week," yelled Roger.

"OK, little children," said the tallest girl. "Meet the players from class 409 here tomorrow at four-thirty. We'll see who can't catch a turtle."

"You're on," said Billy. "Tomorrow is fine."

Soon the older children had gone around the fence and past the bushes.

Then Roger remembered something. "I have to go to the doctor tomorrow."

"It's a good thing tomorrow is Wednesday," said Helen. "Thursday I have to. . . ."

"Tomorrow *is* Thursday," Teddy said.

"Then I can't play," whispered Helen.

"Well," sighed Billy, "come if you can."

When Billy got home, he found his mother taking Connie out of her stroller. Billy had time to hold the baby for a few minutes before she went into her crib to sleep for a while. As he joggled the crib, Billy told his mother about the game.

"You don't mean tomorrow?" asked Mother.

"Sure. Why not?" said Billy.

"Because tomorrow I'm teaching from four o'clock until six o'clock," Mother said.

"That's tomorrow?" Billy stopped joggling the crib. "Are you sure?"

"Yes, I'm sure," Mother said. "And I'm sure that you begged me to let you watch Connie."

Now Billy remembered very clearly. This meant he would have to watch Connie until his father got home at five-thirty.

Smiling a little, Billy said, "I'll watch Connie tomorrow." To himself he thought, "I agreed to play tomorrow. And now I won't even be there. Nice going."

At lunchtime the next day, Billy's friends were very upset.

"But you're our best player," said Paul.

"You agreed to the game, and now you can't play!" said Rosa.

Billy whistled to quiet the clatter. "I'll get to the game as soon as I can," he said.

"You had better hurry. It may be all over before you get there," laughed Paul.

Then they worked on the batting order as they chewed their lunches.

Teddy would have to be in the game because there weren't enough players without him. Everyone was unhappy, but Teddy was the unhappiest of all.

Then Rosa had an idea. "Let's not play at all," she said. "Let's just not show up."

Now Billy began to get angry. "Do we play only when we're going to win? Maybe we will win today. We won't know if we don't play and do our best."

Jane nodded. "We play because we like to, and because it's fun!"

It was a little past five-thirty. They were in the bottom of the last inning. Jane was on first base. There were two outs. They needed two runs to tie it up. The team turned to look at the next batter. It was Teddy.

"Oh, no," Rosa said softly.

"We've lost the game!" hollered Steve.

Just then they heard a whistle.

"It's Billy," shouted Paul. "The game is saved!"

"How are we doing?" asked Billy as he ran up.

"We have only one out left," explained Steve. "We were going to lose, but now you can bat instead of Teddy."

Billy chewed his lip. "I don't think that's fair," he said.

"But it's fine with me," said Teddy quickly. "Let it be someone else's fault if we lose."

"It's not one person's fault," said Billy, shaking his head. "In almost seven innings, there have been twenty outs. One person didn't make them all. We're a team. If we win, it's because we all played well. If we lose, it can't be just one person's fault. That wouldn't be fair."

Rosa watched a bird fly into a bush. Paul looked at the fence. No one looked at Billy because each knew that he was right.

"I have to be home by Saturday," Jane called from first base. "Let's get going."

Rosa handed Teddy the bat. He really didn't want to take it, but he did, whispering, "I'll try my best."

For the first time in his life, Teddy really slugged the ball. By the time someone got the ball, he had dashed to third base. Only then did he think about what he had done.

"I did it!" Teddy hollered. "I did it!" The other players on his team were shouting. So, of course, no one heard him over the clatter.

Paul was up next.

"You can do it," called Rosa.

But Paul struck out. The game was over. Teddy never made it home.

The ball players of class 302 walked to the bench slowly and quietly.

Suddenly Teddy stopped walking.

"Why are we so unhappy?" Teddy asked. "We play to have fun, right? We've lost games before."

"True," said his friends.

"Besides," smiled Teddy, "if I can get to third, we can beat anyone."

"Right," laughed Billy. "OK, team. What do you say we play these clowns again?"

"Let's do it!" they hollered, dashing happily out of the yard.

THINK ABOUT IT

1. What kind of ball player was Teddy? What kind of player was Billy?
2. What had Billy promised to do on the day of the game?
3. Why didn't Billy want to take Teddy's place at bat?
4. Did Teddy get a hit? Who won the game? Why?
5. Did you agree with Billy when he said, "If we lose, it can't be just one person's fault"? Why or why not?
6. Have you ever been on a team? What kind of team was it? Did the team work well together?

How the Sun Came

There was no light anywhere, and the animal people stumbled around in the dark.

"Light!" they said. "We must have light! On the other side of the world, there are people who have light. Maybe they will give us some."

"If they have all the light there is," the fox said, "then they must be greedy people. They won't want to give up any of it. Maybe we should just go and take the light from them."

"Who shall go?" everyone cried. The animals all began talking at once about their speed and strength. Who would be best able to get the light away from the greedy people?

At last the possum said, "I can try. I have a fine, big bushy tail, and I can hide the light inside my fur." He set out at once.

As he traveled eastward, the sun's rays became brighter and brighter until they dazzled his eyes. The possum squeezed his eyes almost shut to keep out the light. That is the way his eyes are to this day.

On and on the possum went with his eyes squeezed almost shut. At last he found the sun. He snatched a piece of it and hid it in his bushy tail. But the sun was so hot, it burned all the fur from his tail. By the time he got home, his tail was as bare as it is today. And he had lost the piece of the sun.

The people still had no light. They still stumbled around in the dark.

"I will go," said the buzzard. "I am not so foolish as to put the sun in my tail."

So the buzzard went. The people who kept the sun were now watching out for thieves, but he flew so high they could not see him.

The buzzard dived southward from the sky and snatched a piece of the dazzling sun in his claws. He set the sun on his head and started for home. But the sun burned off all his head feathers, and he could carry it no longer. That is why the buzzard's head is bald today.

Now the people cried out, "What shall we do? Our brothers have done the best they can do. What else can be done so that we will have light?"

A small voice spoke from the grass. "There may be something I can do," it said.

"Who is speaking?" everyone asked.

"I am Grandmother Spider," the voice replied. "I may be able to bring you light. Who knows? At least I can try."

Then Grandmother Spider felt around in the dark until she found some damp clay. She took a handful of the clay and rolled it into the shape of a small bowl. She started eastward, carrying the damp clay bowl. As she traveled, she spun a thread behind her so that she could find her way back.

She came to the place of the greedy sun people. She was so little and so quiet that no one noticed her. She reached out gently, took a tiny bit of the sun, and placed it in her damp clay bowl.

Then she went back along the thread that she had spun. As she traveled, the damp pottery slowly dried. The sun's light grew and spread before her as she moved westward.

"Thank you, Grandmother," the people said when she returned. "We shall show our gratitude by remembering you always."

The people spoke the truth. Even today the spider's web is shaped like the sun. If you look closely, you can see the sun and its rays.

THINK ABOUT IT

1. Why did the animal people want light?
2. Why did the possum think he should go to get the light?
3. How did the spider get the sunlight?
4. Why are the animals called animal people?
5. Why was it smart of the spider to put the sunlight in a clay bowl?
6. What are other animals that look as if they got too close to the sun?
7. Make up a story about how the rain came.

SUN DANCERS

Sun dancers
Whirling, twirling madly—
Feet churning Mother Earth
Until clouds weep.

Sun dancers
Bringing song to life
With sorrowful drumbeat,
With feathers bright.

Sun dancers
Feathers bowing to four winds,
Feathers dampened by the rain;
Corn feathering on the stalk.

Sun dancers
Throw humble gratitude to sky
In thundering beat
From whirling, churning feet.

Patricia Irving

CRAYON ETCHINGS

Created by Dr. John Lidstone, Queens College of the City University of New York, Consultant in Art Education.

How important are details in a design or a picture? Without the lines that make up the special design of a spider web, the web would look unfinished.

An etching is a special form of art that shows details clearly and interestingly. On the pages that follow, you will experiment with crayon etchings. The results may be amazing.

1

You will need a sheet of manila paper and some bright colored crayons. Do not use dark colors. Pressing hard on your crayons, color every inch of the manila paper.

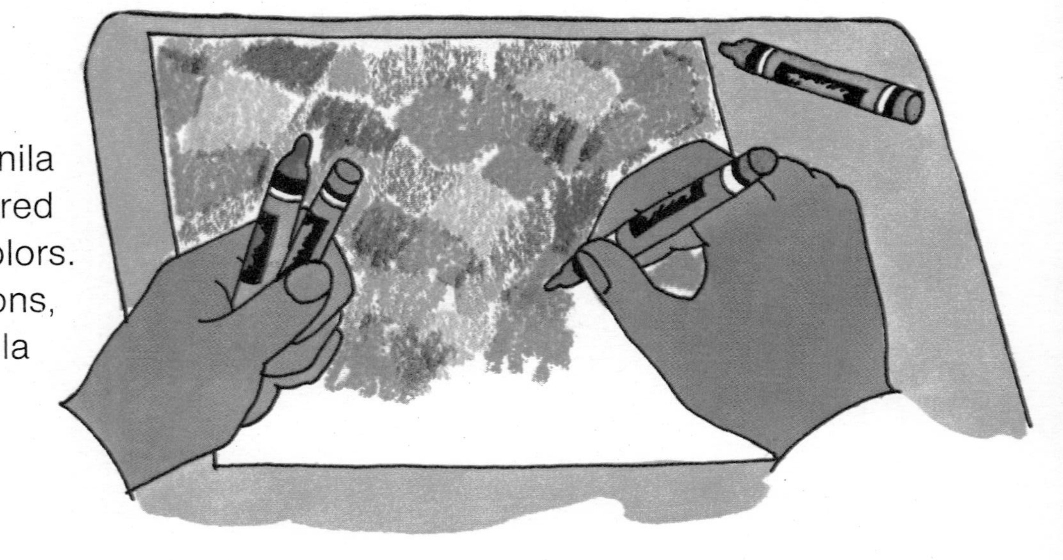

2

Mix thick black poster paint with a little soap.

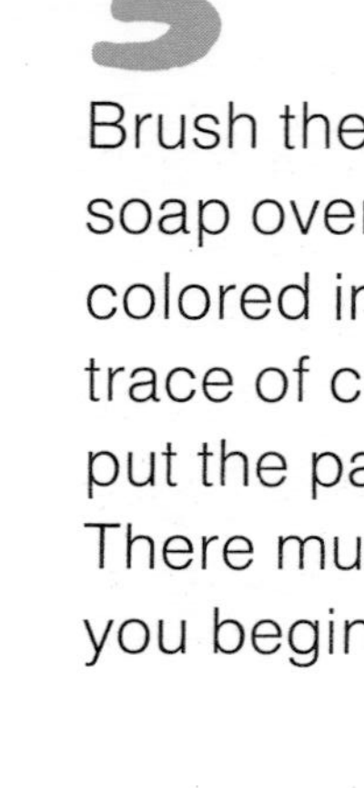

Brush the mixed black paint and soap over the manila paper you colored in step 1. Make sure that no trace of crayon shows through. Then put the painted paper away to dry. There must be no wet spots when you begin etching.

Decide on the picture you want to use for your crayon etching. Sketch it on a plain piece of paper.

5

A paper clip, a pencil, or a hairpin makes a good etching tool. Choose the one you want to use.

6

Keep in mind the design you sketched in step 4. Now use your etching tool to scratch your design on the painted manila paper. Scratch away enough black paint so that the colors beneath the paint show up in your design.

The Necklace

Once, when Maria and I were looking at a store window filled with jewels, we saw a necklace. It had little pieces of metal and glass that looked like real jewels hanging from a gold chain. It was really beautiful!

"I like that!" I said, laughing. "I'll take six!"

But Maria didn't laugh. She just stood staring at the necklace. Then, very softly, she said, "I'm going to buy that necklace."

"But it costs twenty-five dollars!" I said. "How are you going to get that much money?"

"I don't know," Maria said, still staring at the necklace in the window of Jackson's Jewelry Store. "But I will!"

I looked at Maria's face again, and I knew that somehow she'd get the money.

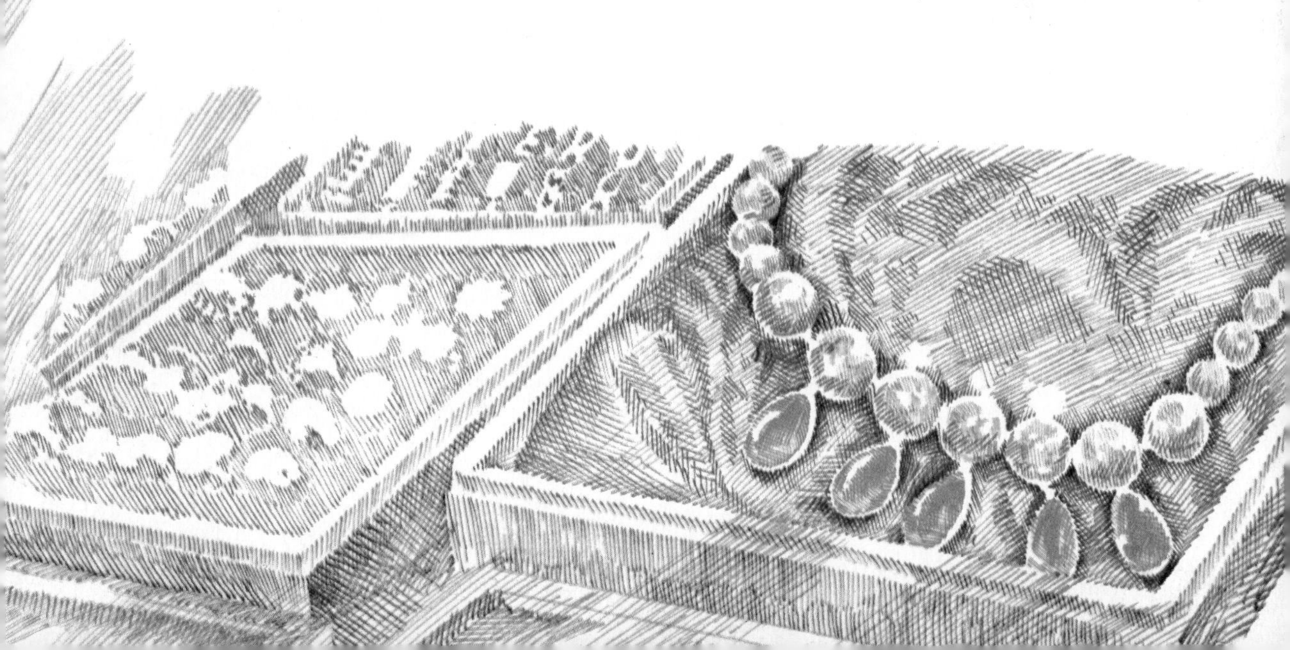

For the next two months, Maria worked after school at Mr. Hutch's TV shop. She'd taken a class in school in how to fix TV sets, so Mr. Hutch was glad to have her help.

Maria was very busy for a while. Then, one night she asked, "Want to come to Jackson's with me tomorrow?"

"You mean, you have the money?" I asked.

"I sure do," she answered, her eyes shining.

Early the next morning we went right down to Jackson's Jewelry Store.

"Good morning. Can I help you?" said Mr. Jackson with a bow. Mr. Jackson had the manner of a gentleman.

"I want to buy that necklace," Maria said softly, pointing to the necklace in the window.

"She has the money, too," I said quickly.

Mr. Jackson offered us a seat. Then he took the necklace out of the window and held it out to Maria. "Let me help you put on this lovely jewel," he said. His manner made her feel like someone very special.

There were tears in Maria's eyes, and her hand was shaking. In a way, I guess I was seeing her for the first time.

Maria is shy and quiet. She is the poet of the family. Her poetry shows warmth and deep feeling—the mark of a true poet. She never gets angry or shouts and hardly ever cries, even when Teresa bosses her around.

Our sister Teresa always bosses Maria around. Teresa's the one who gets the new clothes. When she outgrows them, Maria or I get them as hand-me-downs. We hardly ever get anything of our own that's new. I guess that's why the necklace meant so much to Maria. It wasn't a hand-me-down. It was something all her own that no one had ever used before.

Maria was holding the necklace in her hands. "May I wear it home?" she asked Mr. Jackson.

"Why, of course," he said. "It belongs to you now. Let me help you put it on."

Mr. Jackson held up a mirror so that she could see herself.

Maria smiled. "It's so beautiful," she said. "I've never had anything like it."

When we got home, Maria proudly showed the necklace to Teresa. At first, Teresa was all smiles. Then her face changed and became kind of funny-looking. "Let me try it on," she said. "I want to see how it looks on me."

"Sure," Maria said, handing her the necklace.

Teresa put the necklace on and looked at herself in the mirror. "I want to wear it sometime. OK with you?"

"Well . . . maybe," Maria said. "But first I want to wear it myself for a while."

Maria wore her beautiful necklace only on very special days. Teresa kept after her to borrow it. So one day, Maria finally let her wear it.

"Be careful with it, Teresa, please!" Maria said. "Don't lose it."

Teresa didn't even say thank you. She just left.

"Isn't that just like Teresa!" I said.

"Oh, she means well," said Maria.

That night, when Teresa got home, I knew something was wrong. I could tell by the look on her face. Then it hit me. "You lost the necklace!" I shouted.

"I did not!" Teresa snapped. "It's just broken—that's all."

"Broken!" I said. "How did that happen?"

"It wasn't my fault!" Teresa shouted. "The girls were trying it on, and it just . . . broke."

"Oh, Teresa! How could you let your friends fool around with Maria's necklace like that?" I asked angrily.

I thought of Maria's face, so proud and happy every time she wore her necklace. Then I thought of how her face would look when she found out that her necklace was broken.

I looked at Teresa. "You've got to get it fixed before Maria finds out," I told her.

"Why?" Teresa said. "It wasn't my fault."

"You make me so angry sometimes," I said. "Did you ever stop to think how much that necklace means to Maria? Do you know how hard she had to work to earn it?"

Teresa sat there staring at me. "Look," I offered, "I have some money. I'll go down to the jewelry store and get it fixed."

"You'd do that for Maria?" Teresa asked.

I looked at her and nodded.

"Never mind," she said, "I'll take care of it."

She started toward the door, then stopped and turned around. "Thanks," she said.

It was then that I knew everything was going to be all right between Teresa and Maria. And between Teresa and me!

THINK ABOUT IT

1. How did Maria get the money for the necklace?
2. Why did the necklace mean so much to Maria?
3. How did the sister who told the story feel about Maria?
4. Why wasn't Teresa careful with the necklace?
5. Why did Maria let Teresa wear the necklace?
6. Do you think that Teresa was to blame for the broken necklace?
7. Have you ever broken something that wasn't yours? What did you do about it? How did you feel?

FIND YOUR WAY

In "The Necklace," Maria and her sister go to the jewelry store.

Finding their way around is easy for Maria and Teresa. They know when to turn left or right. They know which streets to cross. But how about you? What might you need to get to Jackson's Jewelry Store? A map would help, wouldn't it?

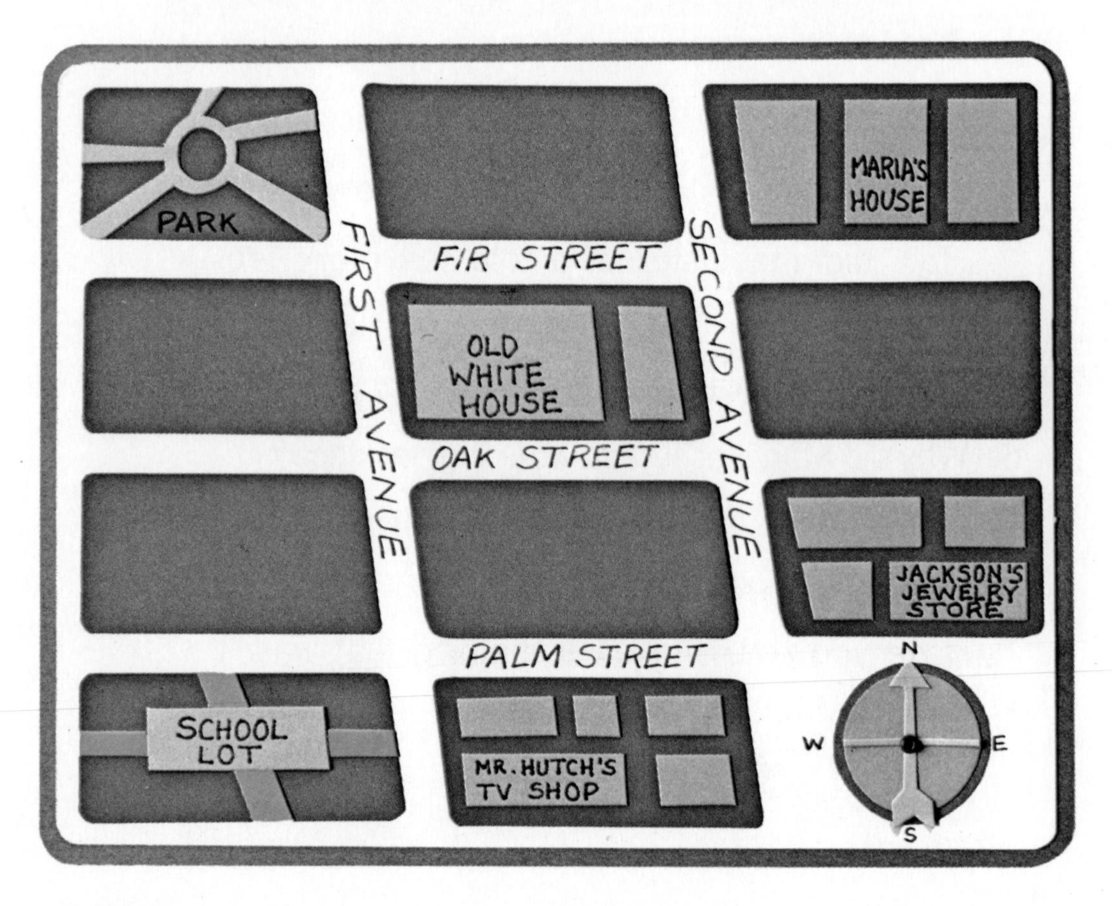

Answer these questions about the map on page 282.

1. Where are north, south, east, and west?

2. What are the three streets shown on the map? Do these streets run from east to west or from north to south?

3. What are the two avenues shown on the map? Do these avenues run from east to west or from north to south?

4. Is Maria's house south or north of Jackson's Jewelry Store?

5. Is the school lot east or west of the TV shop?

6. On what avenue is the old white house? Between which two streets is it?

Here is how Maria gets to Jackson's Jewelry Store from her house. Fill in the missing words by looking at the map.

Walk along ________ Street to _____________ Avenue.
Turn left and walk two blocks to ________ Street.
Turn left to Jackson's Jewelry Store.

Make a map of where you live. On it show your house, your school, and other places to which you go.

Chuka's Hawk

Chuka was standing on the roof of his father's house, keeping well away from the corner where Big Brother kept his pet. As Chuka looked at the pet eagle, he saw the sun. Only a small bit of it showed above the mountains. Big Brother would come home soon to feed the eagle.

Chuka stopped playing and watched the road. Soon he saw Big Brother coming, his bow and arrow in his hand and his hunting bag full.